BREAK-IN

BREAK-IN

Inside the Soviet
Trade Delegation

Bill Graham

THE BODLEY HEAD
LONDON

To my family and friends
who knew nothing about all this

British Library Cataloguing in Publication Data
Graham, Bill
Break-in.
1. Graham, Bill   2. Spies——Great Britain
——Biography
I. Title
327.1'2'0924   UB271.G72G7

ISBN 0–370–31029–2

Photoset by Falcon Graphic Art Ltd
Wallington, Surrey
Printed and bound in Great Britain for
The Bodley Head Ltd
32 Bedford Square
London WC1B 3EL
by Redwood Burn Ltd, Trowbridge, Wilts

First published in Great Britain in 1987

CHAPTER 1

It began with a phone call from Mike Carey of Special Branch inviting me for a drink. The call itself wasn't unusual – Mike and I have been drinking buddies for years – but I know him well enough to recognise the little note in his voice which says he has more on his mind than having a glass or two.

It was November, 1979, and we met on a chilly evening after I had finished work at the little construction company that I run, in partnership with my father-in-law. The pub Mike had chosen was also a sign that he had something special he wanted to talk about. Instead of suggesting one of our locals in North London, near the factory, he asked me to meet him at the Prince Albert in Victoria, near the river, not far from the House of Commons, a pub with plenty of quiet nooks and corners that are made for a discreet chat. Members of Parliament use it a lot. There is a division bell which announces when a vote is being taken in the House, giving MPs eight minutes to scurry back to the division lobbies. Mike Carey uses it when he wants to drag me away from the construction business and into the kind of activities I've been engaged in, on and off, ever since my military service.

After leaving school in Northern Ireland, I joined the Royal Military Police and though I wasn't much more than a kid at the time, I took to the life readily. It wasn't really surprising. A lot of members of my family had served in the forces and I had had both relatives and friends who had been in the RMP so I knew what to expect. After training in England and the usual spells on provost duty – helping to keep off-duty drunken paras from half-murdering off-duty drunken infantrymen in bars around Aldershot – I graduated to the serious stuff and ended up as personal bodyguard to Sir Brian

Kimmons, the Commander-in-Chief of the British Forces in Northern Ireland.

When I came out of the army, I joined the prison service. Next came the security division of the Ministry of Defence, followed by a period as Chief Security Officer of the famous West End department store, Liberty's, before I finally started the family business.

Because of this background, I have a lot of friends in the police and the security services, but among them Mike Carey is something special. We have known each other for a good many years and we have remained friends through all the stages of our lives. At the time of the meeting in the Prince Albert, Mike was in his early forties, slightly younger than myself, and was extremely fit and active. He has always been a keen sportsman. He was a fine rugby player and is now a qualified rugby referee, and he is also a very friendly and relaxed sort of person. He has a way of getting on the right side of people, but for all his easy-going ways, he is also a firm protestant churchman, with strict religious and moral principles. As a policeman he is quick-thinking, efficient and has natural authority, but in undercover work, he has the gift of being able to come across as just an ordinary, likeable chap.

Anyone seeing our meeting in the pub would have put us down as two old pals having a jar after work. We chatted for a while about this and that – the weather, how our families were and how I had done on the horses at the weekend – then, as I had expected, he suggested we move to a quieter part of the pub.

We ordered a couple more pints and took them to a little booth, and it wasn't long before Mike said, 'You know why I called you, don't you? Would you like to do another job for us?'

'You know you can always lead me astray,' I said. 'What kind of job is it?'

'I'll come to that,' he said. 'It's a big one. And it's something a bit different.'

Straightaway, I was on my guard. I thought I knew what was coming next and I thought I was going to have to say no.

Over the years, Mike and I have only ever fallen out over

one thing: I have always refused to work with him against the IRA. He was the one who originally got me involved in police intelligence work, but I told him right from the start that I never wanted to get involved in the Irish situation and I've always stuck to that. I am against terrorism in all its forms, but I was determined not to put my family at risk. I have relatives of both faiths and I knew that if I once got involved in Irish problems I would just get in deeper and deeper until I was completely bogged down and there would be no getting out.

During Mike's early career in the police, this wasn't really a problem. He had spent most of his time in plain clothes in C11, Scotland Yard's criminal intelligence branch, and he originally got me involved because he wanted someone who could pass himself off as a villain. Because of my years in the prison service, that is something I can do quite easily. I have 'done time' in some of the toughest jails in Britain, including Walton in Liverpool, Dartmoor and Parkhurst, and it's quite easy to conceal which side of the bars you are on.

Criminals, especially inexperienced ones, are easily impressed by prison records. If you want to get on the right side of someone who thinks he is jack-the-lad because he has done a few months inside, you only have to say something like: 'Well, if you know so much about doing bird, you tell me how many steps there are down to the punishment block at Walton. . .' and you're off and running.

At various times, I have helped Mike to break a big forgery gang, I have infiltrated a team of armed robbers and helped him set a trap for an escaped murderer. Now, though, Mike's track record in C11 had earned him a transfer to Special Branch. I knew he was pressing hard for promotion to Detective Sergeant and I also knew he was very much involved with IRA terrorism. He had tried once already to get me to help him and I had turned him down. He hadn't liked it, even though he had understood my reasons and now, I was sure, he was going to try me again.

'So what's it all about?' I said again. 'Come on. It's not like you to be coy. Tell me what the job is and I'll give you an answer.'

'I can't tell you yet,' he said. 'I've just been asked to approach you.'

'Who by?'

'By people who know your record and know you'd be willing to cooperate in something that would help your country.'

When he said that, I was sure he was talking about an Irish job and I immediately started to backtrack.

'Bill, it's not what you think,' Mike said. 'And it's absolutely made for you. I can tell you that much.'

I grinned. 'The way you tell it,' I said, 'I'm always made for it. You'd say that if you wanted me to pass myself off as a two-foot pygmy.'

'Bill, I'm serious,' he said. 'Tell me. How's the factory doing?'

'Not bad,' I said. 'Things are a bit slow. Winter's coming on. It's not our best season. What's that got to do with it?'

'Could you use a contract? A really big one?'

'Sure,' I said. 'I'll double glaze Scotland Yard for you any time you want.'

'Bill, for God's sake, be serious.'

'You don't usually mind a joke,' I said. 'What's got into you?'

'I want you to meet some people,' Mike said. 'They're serious people. You can't be casual with them. They'll be watching to see how you handle yourself. I told you. They could guide some business your way. A contract that could really set you up.'

'So there has to be a catch,' I said.

'It's not a catch. The contract comes with the job. It's as simple as that.'

'And you can't tell me what the job is?'

'No. Not yet. Will you let me set up a meeting? In two days time?'

I thought for a moment then I said carefully, 'If you tell me one thing.'

'What's that?'

'That it's not an Irish job.'

I had already decided that if Mike even hesitated over the

8

answer, I was going to end the conversation there and then, but he didn't.

'You have my word,' he said. 'It's nothing to do with the IRA.'

Mike called me back the next day and arranged to see me on the Thursday at seven o'clock. He still didn't give me any more clues and I admit that by the time the meeting came round, I was really intrigued.

The truth is that I really enjoy the kind of jobs I had done for Mike in the past. Frankly, I went into double-glazing only because there is more money to be made in the building trade than there is in the prison service or the Ministry of Defence and I had to think of my family. If it weren't for that, I would have stayed in a job where there was a bit of excitement.

Having Mike as the contact was reassuring too because we have developed a relationship of such trust; even where there are risks, I can count on him not to put me out on a limb unnecessarily. Also, I was just plain curious. If it wasn't the IRA, what else was big enough to justify all the fuss and put Mike in this kind of serious mood?

We met outside Great Portland Street tube station. Mike had warned me that I must be spot on time but that he would be late. That meant a careful security check was being done to see if I was being watched. It was a chilly evening but I had dressed up warmly. I had left work early to give myself time to change into a suit and tie and dark overcoat but it was still nippy standing about in the street. I waited about ten minutes, then Mike appeared, quite casually, as though we had always met like that, and indicated that we were going back down into the tube station.

That meant they were being extra careful. If the meeting place wasn't near this tube station, we were going to be followed by other Special Branch people through the underground to make sure there were no watching eyes.

Mike did not talk much on the way. He wasn't tense exactly but he had the look of someone on his best behaviour and I had the definite feeling that we were really entering the big league, even by his standards.

We took the tube to Pimlico, the area by the Thames near

9

Victoria, again not far from the Houses of Parliament, and walked to the big hotel in Dolphin Square.

The Dolphin Hotel is fairly new. It takes up most of the area on one side of the square and there is a complex which includes luxury flats, restaurants, bars and a swimming pool, as well as the hotel proper. It is not our usual kind of drinking haunt, but Mike seemed to know the layout thoroughly.

We went into the main bar, sat on stools and Mike ordered some beer.

'In a minute, I'm going to leave you,' he said. 'When I come back and give you the nod, we'll go up to room 24. The man you're going to meet is not police. I can't tell you any more until you agree to go ahead.' He grinned. 'And go easy on the jokes. I've told you already. These are serious people.'

When I went up to the room, the first person I met certainly did look serious. The man who opened the door was well over six foot with a craggy face and scar at the side of his left eye. He was dressed in a sports suit and he looked like a rough customer – one of the people who could easily be either cop or villain.

'Bill, this is my boss,' Mike said. 'Detective Chief Superintendent Wade of Special Branch.'

I saw straightaway that this was not the man I had been brought to meet. There was another man in the room, seated at the far end, almost in darkness. The lights had been arranged so that they shone away from him, towards us. It's a trick I had read about but I have to admit that I had never actually seen it used before and I had not realised how effective it is. They were only using ordinary hotel reading lamps but I could not possibly have recognised again the man seated behind them.

Chief Superintendent Wade put out his hand. 'I'm very glad to meet you, Bill,' he said. 'I've heard a lot about you from Mike.'

'As I was asked to bring you here,' Mike said rather formally, 'the Chief Superintendent wanted to be present as my superior officer.'

The man behind the light said nothing. I was straining to make out his features but it was impossible.

'Bill, I know you like a drink,' Wade said. 'We've laid on a few cans.'

I wasn't sure what he meant by the drinking remark and I stayed on my guard. Mike certainly knew that one of my most useful gifts in this line of work is the ability to handle my drink. Even when I appear to be well away, I can keep complete control of my tongue; in all the years I have been doing undercover work, I have never let anything slip. I hoped that was what Chief Superintendent Wade had gathered from the files – not just that I am fond of a glass or two and enjoy the conviviality of pubs.

Wade opened some cans of Long Life and handed me one. The man behind the light still didn't move or say anything.

Wade said quietly, 'Bill, I'm sorry about all this rigmarole, but this gentleman is from one of our élite services. Before you meet him, we have to be certain that this operation is going ahead.'

He had to mean MI5 or MI6. I didn't know which and I had never had any dealings with either, so I wasn't any the wiser. At this point, Mike left and went down to the bar. I sat down, facing the anonymous man behind the light and Wade sat slightly to the side, watching my reactions.

The man began with an apology for what he called 'all this fuss'. He did not sound particularly sorry; still, at least he was observing the courtesies and he gave the impression that he was glad to see me.

He had a very pleasant, educated English voice and I guessed he was at least middle-aged, but there wasn't time for any more peering and gazing because he came straight to the point and pretty soon I had a helluva lot more to think about than what he looked like!

'Mike has told you that we've made a lot of inquiries about you,' he said. 'You've had a fine record with all the departments you have worked with and we're very appreciative of all the unofficial work you have done for the Metropolitan Police in the past. This job, as you'll have gathered, is something different. You run a business which specialises in double-glazing. We'd like you to double-glaze the Soviet Trade Delegation.'

11

I often smile when I think back to that first moment. There I was being asked to spy on the Russians for British Intelligence, but my first reaction, I have to admit, was: 'But that building's enormous.'

I knew the Soviet Trade Delegation Building very well, as I live quite close to it. It stands on the edge of Hampstead Heath, one of the highest points in London, a huge anonymous structure in its own grounds – with an unbelievable number of windows. Never mind the spying; that was a contract any double-glazer would kill to get hold of! Just for a moment I forgot all about who the man behind the light was and what he was really asking me to do. All I could think was: my company is about to hit the big time.

The man behind the light must have seen my reaction but he only said lightly, 'I don't have to tell you that there will be another side to the job.'

I laughed. 'Yes,' I said, 'I do understand that. And I'd like to know more about it.'

'I can't give you details until you are sure you're going ahead with it. What I can tell you is that it will be a purely observational job.'

I asked what kind of observation, but he would not be drawn. He did not mention bugging or any other spying activities as such. The word he kept coming back to was 'observation'. He said it was extremely rare for the intelligence services to get this close to the Russians and he tried to reassure me by saying they would definitely not risk blowing the opportunity by taking too many chances.

When I look back on what the operation finally grew into, that first conversation seems almost comical. I knew, of course, that I was being gently sucked in but these introductory meetings are a game and both sides know the rules and make a pretence of observing them.

'What we need first,' the man said, 'is your basic commitment to work with us.'

Even as I was weighing the risks, I was still thinking about the business side and I said: 'You must know that Palace Glazing is a very small company. Most of the contracts we normally handle are for under a thousand pounds. At the

12

moment, we're not geared for anything this big. It would mean a lot of changes: hiring more men, deals with new suppliers. I'm in partnership with my father-in-law. He would have to be involved in any new financial arrangements.'

The man did not seem bothered by this. 'First, give us your answer,' he said. 'If it's yes, we'll solve all those problems.'

By now, I was beginning to get really excited and I have to confess that it was mainly at the prospect of making some real money out of an operation. I'm not actually as mercenary as this makes me sound, but, usually, whatever else you get out of intelligence work, it isn't money and I felt, secretly, that I had earned a financial break after all the risks I had taken in the past. The job did not sound as dangerous as some of the things I had done before and it certainly sounded a lot more profitable. I almost made up my mind there and then, but I decided that it would look better if I took a little time to consider the situation.

'Can you give me twenty-four hours to think about it?' I asked.

'Of course,' he said. 'Mike will arrange another meeting.'

I went downstairs to the bar and found Mike looking even more thoughtful than before. 'Let's go somewhere a bit more cosy,' he said, 'and you can tell me what happened. There's a good pub on the other side of the square.'

We walked across Dolphin Square and Mike stayed very quiet and subdued. I was feeling exhilarated. I wanted to talk but I also wanted to draw Mike out and see what he really thought about the situation, so I forced myself to stay quiet too and let him make the running.

In the pub, Mike bought the beer and, finally, he began to loosen up.

'Well,' he said. 'Now that you know what it's about, what did you say?'

'I said I'd think it over. I have until tomorrow.'

'And . . . ?' he said inquiringly.

'Tell me what you think first,' I said. 'You're the one who got me into this.'

'Bill, we've been pals a long time,' Mike said. 'I'm not going to try and kid you. At this moment, you're the fish and

I'm the angler. I've told them I can land you, and they're sitting on the bank watching to see if I can deliver. Landing you can do me a lot of good. I'm coming up for promotion. You don't usually make sergeant at the first try. This could clinch it.'

I grinned. 'That kind of blackmail is going to cost you another pint.'

'Yes, I know it's blackmail,' Mike said, 'but we're still friends and I'm worried about one thing.'

'What's that?'

'That you'll underestimate these people. The Russians. We've done a lot of jobs together and I've seen how you handle yourself. But we've always dealt with people you're really at home with. Villains are right up your street. You've lived among them. You know how they talk, how they think. Have you ever even spoken to a Russian?'

'No,' I said, 'not really.'

'Well, compared to the crowd you usually mix with on building sites, they're all going to seem like perfect gentlemen. But they're not. Their intelligence people are deadly. You've never worked with the white collar brigade before. I'm just afraid you won't take them seriously enough.'

I could tell from Mike's tone that this really was a friend talking. It was not an extra layer of blackmail. He wanted me to take the job, but he didn't want to land me in it, just so he would get a promotion.

'If you were me, what would you do?' I said.

'I'd take it,' Mike said, 'but I'd look in the mirror every morning and say to myself "you just be fucking careful".'

'Don't worry,' I said. 'I'll be careful. I am going to take it. Christ, what kind of a double-glazer would I be if I turned down a contract like that.'

This time, Mike did not bother to tell me to stop joking. He knew I was making a serious decision and I did not have to spell out for him the reasons I had for agreeing, apart from the money. We have known each other too many years for it to be necessary. You don't talk about patriotism to an old mate in a pub and anyway, Northern Irelanders understand about loyalty to the flag, without making a song and dance about it. It had been bred into both of us.

Mike knew too that I like the excitement of working with him. For me, the challenge is the thrill of matching wits with dangerous people. I am not at all the James Bond type. I would never be the hunter-killer type of agent. That is not my style at all. If I am threatened directly, I will have a go with anyone. I am not worried about looking after myself. You don't last long in the RMP or on a landing in Walton jail if you can't handle trouble. But I couldn't honestly pull the trigger on anyone in cold blood. I have worked with people who can, but I am not one of them.

Surprisingly, perhaps, it was my time among really violent people in the prison service that shaped my attitude to undercover work more than anything else. I learned in prison that you have to master dangerous people mentally. You cannot subdue them for long by physical violence. When I go undercover, I get a real kick out of going up against someone who thinks he is a master criminal and taming him without his ever knowing how he's been tamed. I could see why Mike was concerned about this new kind of opponent, but I was not really worried. Whatever anyone said, I could not really believe that it was going to be worse than some of the things I had got up to before.

I told Mike there and then that I was going ahead and there was no need to wait twenty-four hours for the answer. After that, we dropped the subject and settled down to a really enjoyable night's drinking and Mike set up another meeting at The Dolphin for the next day.

I met him again at Great Portland Street and we went through the same routine, except that this time we entered The Dolphin through a side door and went to a different room.

The other big difference was that there were no lights shielding the face of the person I was there to meet, and I found myself face to face for the first time with the man whom I came to know as Jay.

I had guessed his age right – somewhere in his early fifties – and he was smartly dressed in a city suit. On the chair was a loose-fitting swagger overcoat and a fisherman's tweed hat which I was to come to regard as Jay's trademark. He almost always wore it and it gave him a vaguely Sherlock Holmes look, even though it wasn't a deerstalker.

He apologised straightaway for the way I had been treated on the last occasion but said he was sure I would understand that it had to be like that. His manner was very relaxed and I felt immediately at home in his company. Considering how many hours I was going to spend talking to him in the months to come it was just as well, but at that stage, it was strictly a first impression; I knew nothing about him other than that he was a senior intelligence officer who was in direct and personal charge of the operation.

He told me openly now that he was with MI6 and he explained briefly that his service normally operated outside the United Kingdom while MI5 dealt with threats to the internal security of the country, but as the Soviet Trade Delegation, like an embassy, was technically foreign territory, it came within his jurisdiction.

Most of the evening was spent talking about my background. Jay said he wanted to get to know me and we went over at great length all my government service. He obviously knew the whole story already but he asked me a lot of detailed questions, especially about work I had done involving observation. At the Ministry of Defence I had spent quite a lot of time doing security vetting, or rather preparing reports for the boards who vetted MoD personnel.

When an officer is posted to the Ministry of Defence in Whitehall it is often the first time he has worked in civilian clothes and away from his unit or regiment. He takes off his uniform, joins the pinstripe brigade and straightaway feels elated and a bit superior – and often too much at his ease.

To guard against this, he is observed closely right from his first days in Whitehall. Security officers follow him home after work and watch him on evenings and weekends. For the person doing the following, it is a straightforward job of routine observation. The results go down on a checksheet. Where he drinks: bar, pub or club. How many drinks taken and what kind. Does he drink usually in male or female company? What kind of companions? How much does he

16

spend? Does he drive after drinking? Or visit betting shops ... and so on ... there is a box for everything.

Inside the MoD building too, much of the security work is straight observation. Every room is checked every day and every night for signs of security lapses. They can be glaringly obvious like a briefcase left in the toilet, or tiny, like a fragment of carbon left in a waste basket when it should have been shredded.

I joked with Jay about one of my commendations, a personal one from Lord Louis Mountbatten who was Chief of the Defence Staff while I was at the MoD. In a serious incident that was hushed up at the time, a ceremonial sword was stolen from his office and I was the person who found it. When the sword went missing, Mountbatten's personal fury was awesome enough on its own, but there had been press reports recently of several security lapses in government departments and it was feared that if word got out, the headlines would be never-ending.

I accidentally found the sword, hidden behind a cupboard in another office, during one of my night rounds. We never did find out who took it or why. It could have been a joke, or someone trying to prove security was lax, or it could have been someone who had intended to steal it, but had got cold feet about getting it out of the building.

All in all, Jay put me through a couple of hours of subtle and very thorough interrogation. I didn't raise any objections. I knew it had to be gone through, but by the end of the evening I was beginning to feel it was my turn to ask a few questions.

When I started to probe, Jay was friendly, but not very forthcoming, so finally I asked him outright a question that had been very much on my mind.

'We've talked a lot about observation,' I said, 'but I presume you already know who you want me to observe. Your service must surely have a lot of information already about who are the spies inside the Soviet Trade Delegation.'

His answer, for once, for equally direct.

'No, Bill,' Jay said, 'we don't. We have identified a few of course. But your main task will be to help us find the rest.

17

Think of it this way. There are between 630 and 650 people at the Trade Delegation at any one time – quite apart from the huge staff at their embassy in Kensington.

'In theory, their movements are restricted, but in reality it's impossible to keep track of them all. It would take an army of people to do round-the-clock surveillance of over 600 people. In fact we don't even have enough resources to follow just the ones we think *might* be engaged in intelligence activities.

'Most of them are there for quite legitimate tasks. Your main job is to help us pinpoint the ones who are worth watching.

'In all the years we have been trying, we have never had a better chance of cutting down our own work and finding out who the targets ought to be. That's what we want from you, Bill. It's simple, but it's vitally important.' Jay smiled.

'I know you're very interested in the business side of this thing too,' he said, 'and that's our first priority too. You'll be getting a letter soon inviting you to the embassy. Your first task is to clinch the contract. Without that, the operation won't even get off the ground. So just make sure you make a good impression.'

CHAPTER 2

One thing that sticks in my mind about my first visit to the Soviet Trade Delegation is the profusion of squirrels. They were everywhere, running across the paths and scurrying up and down the trees in the grounds. I remember being surprised that the Russians hadn't hunted them to extinction because they made the place look untidy; it seemed a nice little human touch to offset the cold officialdom I was expecting to encounter. I remember too, though, Jay's clear warning: 'Don't underestimate these people,' and I soon had my mind strictly focused on business.

Since my first meetings with Jay, I had received a letter from a North London company inviting me to subcontract for the double-glazing of the Soviet Trade Delegation building. I did not know the company and Jay would tell me nothing about it. Reading between the lines, and from fragments I picked up later, I gathered it was a small family firm which had done repair work on Soviet buildings for many years. The owner had either died or retired and MI6 had kept it going. This seemed to be a kind of pattern, with MI6 taking an interest in all the companies which did business with the Russians in London and not allowing any contacts to lapse.

I then received a phone call from the Trade Delegation itself from a man who introduced himself as Mr Denushenko, inviting me to come and discuss the contract and take measurements. The odd thing about that call was that Denushenko talked as though there was no doubt I would be doing the job, whereas usually, at the tendering stage, everything is much more uncertain. Anyway, it was a hopeful sign, and I went to see Denushenko in confident mood.

The Soviet Trade Delegation is a massive building in one of the highest parts of Highgate, overlooking a quiet corner of Hampstead Heath. It was built at the turn of the century and

19

the Soviets have owned it for many years, adding to it here and there. Overall, it is quite a pleasant-looking building, mainly because of the grounds which have some very fine trees and shrubs and a small ornamental waterfall outside the main entrance.

It is one of the very quietest parts of London; there are a few exclusive homes nearby, owned by wealthy businessmen and the occasional Arab diplomat. A main road passes near one side, but the building is well shielded by a wall and tall hedges, and the other sides give on to quiet side roads or the open ground of the heath.

We entered the grounds through a pair of double iron gates, past the first security check, and parked in a small car park, off the main drive. I had given a lot of thought to the impression I wanted to make and I had gone for a mixture of business-like and workman-like. I was dressed in a suit and carried a briefcase, but I had gone in the company van, driven by Kevin Daley, one of my senior workmen, who was dressed tidily but in his site clothes. I was smart, but not too smart to emphasise that I was a working director and between us, we looked as though we were ready for anything: negotiations, paperwork – or measuring up.

I left Kevin in the van and went alone up the main entrance which had double glass doors. I pushed one of them but it did not open. There did not seem to be any doorbell or intercom, but I could see a reception desk on the other side and my arrival had obviously been noted because I heard an electric buzzer and one of the doors opened.

The reception area was pretty standard. Behind the counter, there were two young women. One was operating an old-fashioned telephone switchboard; the other was the receptionist and she took my name, asked what company I was with, made a call and said, 'Mr Denushenko will be with you shortly.'

Denushenko came straightaway and he was certainly the kind of man who makes an immediate impact. He was a big man, around six foot in height, in his sixties, with grey hair, dressed in a smartly cut sports coat and slacks. His face was slightly chubby but there was nothing soft about his handshake. He gripped my hand as though he were testing to see if my wrist would unscrew and when I retrieved it, you could see faint white welts from the pressure.

Apart from that, his welcome wasn't at all aggressive. He greeted me courteously, and took me past another security guard into an area where there were three small offices, obviously interview rooms for people coming to the Trade Delegation on business. We went into one of them and Denushenko ordered coffee and biscuits, which were brought in by a young woman who just put them down, without saying anything.

In the months that followed, I got to know the key figures in the Trade Delegation so well that it is hard to recall them as the shadowy figures they appeared on that first day. The woman who brought the coffee I now know as Martia – I ended up seeing as much of her almost as I do of my own office secretary, but at that stage I did not even know her name. She was simply a rather attractive young woman, with dark hair tied back tightly, carrying a tray of refreshments.

Denushenko spoke excellent English, with only a slight accent. He explained that they wanted the whole Trade Delegation complex double-glazed but they wanted to proceed by stages, and he asked me what I needed to do before submitting estimates. I told him how the estimates would be calculated, with a price based on the measurement of each individual window, with a supplement for any window needing more than one opener. I also made it clear there would be a separate charge, calculated by the running foot, if the wooden frame of the original window had to be replaced.

Denushenko said that was fine but he added one stipulation I had not expected: if any wooded frames had to be replaced, the wood we used must be Iroko. It was a timber I had never used – and it turned out to be a devil to screw and drill – but I wanted to keep the customer happy and if that was all it was going to take, that was fine by me.

'I want you to measure first what we call our hotel,' Denushenko said. 'Someone will accompany you while you work, then come back here to meet me, when you have finished.'

I was amazed at how quickly and smoothly it seemed to be going, and I went to fetch Kevin.

Our escort was someone else I came to know very well – a man called Ivan Koften. At that stage, no name was used. I was simply handed over to Ivan who my workmen later named Mighty Mouse, because he was built like a weight-lifter but in miniature; a muscly, powerful man but very short so that he looked like a scaled-down version of a much bigger athlete.

What Denushenko had called the hotel was the building which formed a large part of the back of the complex, and my first impression was that it was much more of a hostel than a hotel. A typical room was furnished with a single bed and a plain dressing table and wardrobe. There were no sinks or toilets in the rooms, only communal washing facilities and lavatories on the landings. It was carpeted throughout and the carpets, though very old, were quite decent and the building gave the overall impression of being kept very clean. The hostel feeling was emphasised on the third floor where there was a big communal canteen, obviously designed not for meal service, but for residents to do their own cooking. There was a kitchen with several cookers, fridges and freezers and there were pots and pans here and there with food in that seemed to have been left overnight for reheating. The main room had very much the air of a works canteen with rows of tables and simple chairs, and though the cooking equipment was modern, the general atmosphere was pretty spartan. I noticed also that although the canteen seemed to cater for a great many people, there was only one TV set.

I did not examine anything too closely, though. As we went from room to room, Mighty Mouse unlocked each door, then stood in the doorway watching us work. I made a point of not seeming at all nosy. I walked into each room and went straight to the window, giving it my full attention, then as we left, the door was locked behind us. The measuring-up job took the best part of two hours and throughout, Ivan did not say a single word. I thought it was probably because he was not very confident in English, and I found out later that I was right; still, it was a bit unnerving to be watched by someone quite as grim and I wondered whether all our work was going to be supervised so diligently and with so little warmth or humour.

When we had finished, I was taken back to the office and when Denushenko arrived, he was with another man who was introduced as Mr Bartov. He was also in his sixties and though he did not say much, he listened very intently to what went on between myself and Denushenko. I guessed, rightly again, that Bartov was Denushenko's boss, there to oversee the negotiation.

In fact, negotiation was not the right word at all. All Denushenko seemed interested in was how quickly the prices could be worked out. Eventually, I made a comment to test the water. I said that I didn't want to appear over-confident but was I right to assume that I had a good chance of being selected? I added a few comments about how pleased I was to be considered, especially as the firm would gain considerable prestige from undertaking work on behalf of an organisation like the Soviet Trade Delegation.

Denushenko would not commit himself but nothing he said gave me any cause for concern.

'If your prices are satisfactory, it will go ahead,' he said. 'We are aware of the prices of aluminium and other materials. If you bring the estimates tomorrow, we will give you an answer there and then.'

I dropped in a little salesman's line about how nice it would be if all contracts could be arranged so efficiently and Denushenko said, 'We will see you tomorrow morning. Please come at eight o'clock.'

I tried to make a little joke. 'Mr Denushenko,' I said, 'if you had said six o'clock, I would be there.'

As a joke, the remark was a total washout. Denushenko said in deadpan tones, 'No. Not six o'clock. The gates are not open until eight o'clock. That is when we start work.'

I made a mental note that however good Denushenko's English was, he certainly didn't have much of an Irish sense of humour!

I went back to the factory, called Mike and told him that I had to submit estimates by the next morning. 'Christ, that's quick,' Mike said. 'I'll get onto Jay and set up a meeting.'

I spent a couple of hours pricing the order, then I took the draft down to The Dolphin Hotel the same evening. Jay was crisp and business-like.

'Right,' he said, 'what do the figures look like?'

I told him that the first part of the contract – the section Denushenko called the hotel – the cost would be about £11,000.

'Is that a realistic figure?' Jay asked. 'We have to be careful. We mustn't scare them off with overpricing, but if we pitch it too low, they may smell a rat.'

'It's a very fair price,' I said. 'It gives me a reasonable profit margin, but there are no allowances for special problems or breakages.' I grinned at Jay. 'I bore in mind your promise that you'd cover me for any losses.'

Jay smiled. 'Don't worry,' he said, 'we'll stick to our part of the bargain. You won't lose money on the deal. It sounds as though you've got exactly the right price for what we need.'

'They should be happy,' I said. 'I've treated them as though I really want their business. If they know as much about prices as they say they do, they'll recognise that. I wouldn't have gone much higher anyway. I learned a long time ago that it never pays to get too cocky. They're behaving as though this contract is in the bag, but I've lost count of the number of times I've thought that, then lost the deal at the very last minute.'

'That's fine,' Jay said. 'But be careful how you handle yourself tomorrow. If you get the contract, be natural. Go straight back to the factory and break the news. Tell everyone. It's a big contract; it'll set the factory up for months. Organise some drinks. Make it a real celebration – then call Mike, and we'll set our side of things rolling.'

I was back at the Trade Delegation the next morning at five minutes to eight. The gates were not open and we deliberately parked right outside, where we could be seen, to show our eagerness.

When we were let in, Denushenko arrived promptly and I was taken to the same interview room and given more coffee and biscuits. I had not yet got the hang of dealing with Denushenko, but I decided I would try a little comment to see if I could break through his formal manner. I had had no

24

dealings with Russians but I do a lot of business with Greeks and I always find that a compliment or sympathetic comment about their country never goes amiss.

As Denushenko got up to leave I said, 'Mr Denushenko, before you make your decision, I'd just like to say how proud I am to have been considered for this contract. One of the great memories of my boyhood was watching Arsenal play Moscow Dynamo and I never thought I'd be dealing with the Russian people like this. Win or lose, it has been a pleasure.'

I thought at first I had misjudged him and he was going to remain stone-faced, but I saw quickly that I'd make a right move and he responded to the remark very well.

'I'll be back in ten minutes,' Denushenko said – and vanished for three quarters of an hour.

It seemed like a very long wait. There was nothing to read in the waiting room and I passed the time going through some papers in my briefcase, but when Denushenko did finally return, I could see straightaway from his smile that everything was OK.

'The figures you have presented are satisfactory,' Denushenko said. 'We would like you to begin straightaway. I understand you have to take more technical measurements before you can order the materials.'

I didn't know who he had been talking to, but he had the procedure exactly right. I said yes, that was correct and how soon could I start.

'When you are ready, ring for an appointment,' Denushenko said. 'We will say yes or no depending on whether it is convenient. You must understand that at no time will your workmen or yourself be allowed to move through the building without escorts. This has to be arranged in advance, so you must always make appointments.'

I said I understood, naturally, that embassies had to be careful about security, but I also said that I could certainly vouch for the honesty of my men.

'Nevertheless,' Denushenko said, 'any work that is done for the Soviet people must be carefully supervised.'

We parted finally on very friendly terms. I thanked him for all his help in putting the order through quickly and made a joke about how much I would enjoy buying him a drink if we weren't on official premises.

As I left, I made no effort to hide my excitement. I almost ran to the van to give the news to Kevin, then I followed Jay's instructions to the letter. We went back to the factory, broke the news, then I invited several of the workmen to a nearby pub for a celebration.

After an hour or so, I left them to it, called Mike, then took a taxi down to join him at another pub in Victoria, called The Shakespeare. It is a pub Mike and I have used many times for meetings because it has a basement and there are three entrances, so it is very easy to slip in and out by different doors.

I had told Mike already on the phone that everything had gone well, but the first thing he said to me was: 'Have you got anything in writing?'

'No,' I said, 'but I'm quite sure they mean to go ahead. They didn't seem to have any reservations at all. When I've taken final measurements and prepared an estimate with details of the materials, we'll both sign it and that would normally be our agreement.'

'Jay is going to be elated,' Mike said. 'You stay here and have a couple of drinks. I'll be back in an hour.'

When he came back, he didn't even sit down. 'Drink up,' he said, 'we're off to Dolphin Square. From now on, the pressure really goes on.'

'What pressure?' I said. 'I did exactly as you said and we got the contract.'

Mike grinned. 'Yes. We got the contract,' he said, 'but just try to remember that this is not just about double-glazing.'

The meeting at Dolphin Square began as a celebration and very quickly turned into a serious briefing session. Jay had brought a bottle of eight-year-old Bell's scotch and we had a couple of drinks to relax while I told him exactly what had happened at the meeting with Denushenko.

'It sounds perfect,' Jay said. 'It's taken us a very long time to get to this stage. Now we can get down to the real work.' He grinned. 'It's time to organise the photo album.'

Jay explained that he had collected together every single

26

photograph they possessed of the 650 people in the Trade Delegation. Most of them were passport photos, filed with applications for entry into Britain, but they also had many other photos too, and they were all being put into one 'album'. The names and official details were being put on the back of each photograph. I was going to be asked to spot them by the picture only, then give the name I knew them by, if any, and we would then turn over the photo and compare my information with the official data.

Jay explained that they had had a lot of trouble in the past with the accuracy of the photos – and even of the names. Some of the confusion was caused by the fact that passport photos are notoriously bad anyway, but Jay was sure that some of it was deliberate and they had come across cases where wigs, moustaches and changed hair colour had been used to deceive deliberately.

Jay also went through in great detail all the things he wanted me to observe, right down to the licence numbers of British cars visiting the Trade Delegation. He also gave me a few reminders about technique – warning me, for example, never to write any names or car licences down where I could be seen, but to memorize them then jot them down in the toilet. He told me nothing I didn't know already, but I was reassured by Jay's obvious concern for attention to detail.

Next, Jay turned to the workmen I would be using.

'We'd like you to use a mainly Irish team,' he said. 'We reckon the Russians might be reassured by that. You're from Northern Ireland but most of your men are from the South, and anyway, I don't suppose the Russians are very hot on Irish accents. Our feeling is that they might be less suspicious of you if they thought you were a bit anti-British. Make no mistake, Bill, the Russians will monitor your men's conversations on the site.'

I laughed. 'That'll be a treat for them. If they do, they'll hear the same talk they'd hear on any building site in the world: women, booze and football.'

Jay laughed too, then he produced an official file on each of my men. 'You know this one has a criminal record, don't you,' he said, indicating one of my best craftsmen.

'Yes, I know,' I said, 'but that was a long time ago. He's a good man and anyway, there aren't many building firms in London that don't have someone on site who's done a bit of time.'

'We're not worried about the record,' Jay said, 'as long as you're sure he's straight now.' We don't want you kicked off the job because some clown starts nicking things.'

'There's no chance,' I said. 'I'll vouch for him.'

I was getting a bit defensive by this time because Jay had obviously been through my men's backgrounds with a fine toothcomb.

'I know you want Irishmen,' I said, 'but there's one Greek I want to use. He's one of my best fitters.'

'That's no problem,' Jay said, 'He fits in with the non-British angle just as well. So that looks as though that's squared away. Oh and by the way,' Jay added casually, 'from now on it will be you and me. Mike will be dropping out.'

The remark stopped me dead in my tracks. Up to that point everything had been very amiable and straightforward, unfolding exactly as we had agreed and planned. This was something completely unexpected and it really worried me.

'Jay, when I undertook to do this,' I said, 'we agreed that Mike would be my contact man.'

'I know,' Jay said, 'but unfortunately, there are problems with that. With Mike, we could be treading on very dangerous ground. There are strict rules about what the Metropolitan Police, even Special Branch, can be involved in.'

'That may be,' I said, 'but that should have been pointed out before. I'm not superstitious, but I just don't believe in changing a winning team. I'm not trying to mess you about. I've got the contract and I'm damned glad to have it, but I definitely want Mike in on this.'

I went on at great length about how well Mike and I worked together; how we knew each other's routines and could coordinate without even thinking about it. If we were supposed to be meeting, for example, we could pass signals to each other almost telepathically if either sensed something was going wrong and we could ignore each other without anyone suspecting we were old friends.

'Apart from anything else,' I said, 'we're both Northern Irelanders. We have our own little ways.'

Jay argued back equally strongly. He went over all the arguments about how risky it was to involve the police in what was essentially a foreign operation. He tried to convince me that we wouldn't need special techniques for arranging our debriefing meetings. We were going to stop using Dolphin Square and they were setting up what Jay called a 'shop' – a secure flat in central London which I could enter and be sure of having my back fully covered.

I listened but I simply wasn't buying. To be absolutely frank, I just didn't trust Jay enough yet to have him replace Mike.

I had nothing at all against Jay, but in the field you learn only to trust people you've known for a long time and worked with in difficult situations. Jay was pleasant enough and he seemed straightforward and easy to get on with. Still, I knew nothing about his background. I found out later that Jay was a very experienced field officer who had worked in Moscow and I came to have great respect for his skills as a controller and debriefer and for his ability to foresee developments during the assignment.

At that point, all I knew about him was that he was a senior officer from MI6, which I had always regarded as the dark side of the security services, and he was no substitute for Mike. There's a rule in the army – and it applies in intelligence and most other fields for that matter – when there is a buck to be passed, it passes downwards, and I did not know how far Jay would go to protect me if things started to go wrong. With Mike, I never had any doubts. He would yell and scream at me sometimes for taking chances he didn't think necessary, but he was always on my side, right or wrong, but there was no way I could say the same about Jay. Finally, Jay admitted that my insistence on keeping Mike made sense and he promised to try to get clearance from his superiors. That took twenty-four hours, and when word came through that it had been agreed, both Mike and I were delighted. Mike very much wanted to stay involved and he knew I would make a fuss, but I think even he was surprised at how strongly

I felt about it – and the knowledge made us an even stronger team.

Very quickly, the final arrangements were made. I got the factory ready for a rapid expansion of the business and re-organised our finances, while Jay and Mike finished the preparations on the security side. Mike told me – on the quiet – that his Special Branch warrant card had been withdrawn and his details removed from the police computer, just in case the Russians had access to it. For the same reason my own official file was doctored. All reference to my RMP and Ministry background was erased and I was made out to have leftish leanings; not exactly red tendencies, but definitely anit-Thatcher and pro the working class.

I made arrangements with Denushenko to get the work properly underway and it was then that Jay gave me a final caution.

By now, he was very much at ease with me, and his briefings were usually delivered with a dry sense of humour, but he gave me the warning with total seriousness.

'Just remember,' he said, 'if the Russians do tumble to what your're doing, there isn't a lot we can do to help you. In that Trade Delegation, they are on their own ground. They can do what they like and there's not much we can do about it. . .

'Four years ago,' he continued, 'Highgate police got a call to say they wanted to notify a death. It was a Soviet colonel with a broken neck and we never found out how he died or why. All we did was allow them to make arrangements to ship the body back to the Soviet Union.

'Even though you're not a Russian, our hands would still be tied. You'll be working on some high windowsills and God knows where else. If you had a fall, we couldn't even investigate properly after the event.'

I tried to turn the caution into a joke, but Jay would not let me take it lightly.

'I'm not trying to scare you,' he said quietly. 'I just want you to understand once and for all that you're not really going to be working in Highgate. To all intents and purposes, you are about to enter the Soviet Union.'

CHAPTER 3

'My name is Marat. I am your guard.'

The man was big, muscular, well over six foot, smartly dressed in a dark suit, a formal white shirt and a black tie with a red stripe.

His greeting was pleasant enough but I was aware, as we chatted at the entrance to the Trade Delegation, that the success of at least the first part of my mission could well hinge on how I got on with this man. Would he be strict or casual? Helpful or obstructive? In a word, was he going to be jailer or companion?

It was a fine, sunny winter morning, in January 1980. The preliminaries had gone smoothly and the contract was signed. We were about to start work and the ground rules had been laid down very forcefully by Mr Denushenko: each workman, myself included, would have an individual guard who would act as escort wherever we went in the Trade Delegation complex.

Marat spoke good English, accented but clear, and he seemed like an educated man, not a mindless heavy, which might work for me or against me – I wasn't yet sure which.

We walked together into the building and, as with any normal job, we began with a chat to the person who was responsible for the day-to-day running of the building, in this case, Martia, a motherly but rather tough-looking middle-aged woman who was in charge of the hotel.

As with any normal job too, her main concern was how much mess we were going to make. I promised her that we would always put down dust sheets and be as tidy as possible. To Marat, it was only a routine exchange, but I was thinking fast. The arrangements I made now could be crucial in determining how much freedom of movement I would have.

'Our usual system is to work on two rooms at once, and

prepare two more at the same time, so that the fitters keep busy,' I told Martia.

It wasn't our usual system at all, but I had already counted five guards, including Marat. Working on four rooms would spread them thinly, especially as, at most times three of the guards would have to be outside watching the fitters who were working on the exterior of the windows. As overall supervisor, I would have to be able to move from room to room, and I guessed that unless Marat was especially diligent, he would get fed up with following me everywhere and would rely on other guards being in some of the rooms. When both he and Martia accepted the two-plus-two system without question, I felt I had already scored an important little victory.

I chatted for a few minutes to Martia, checking on details like where to find cleaning liquid and buckets, then, with more promises to keep her hotel as clean as we could, I went off with Marat to the first bedroom.

The room was obviously occupied, but it was empty when we went in and I assigned two fitters to start removing the big outside window.

The Trade Delegation was certainly in need of double-glazing. The windows themselves weren't in bad condition, in fact the frames were mostly pretty solid, but the sashes had dropped and warped and there were gaps everywhere. On cold days, the wind whistled through, especially in the rooms facing across Hampstead Heath.

Before the men started work, I made a point of giving them a few instructions. They knew perfectly well what to do – they had all been with me for long enough – but they understood that the orders were for the benefit of the client. I had emphasised to Denushenko that I was very much a working director and would always be on site to supervise every stage of the contract. Again, though, there was more to it than that: the style of work I had told my men to adopt was going to be one of my main methods of prolonging the contract.

I had told the fitters that during the negotiations for the contract I had gathered that the Russians were absolute perfectionists; they were not impressed by speed, they wanted the highest quality workmanship. It wasn't true but it sounded plausible and my chaps didn't care anyway; they were paid by the hour, not the contract, and they didn't mind if the work lasted until their retirement. I told them to do everything strictly by the book. I wanted screws placed exactly nine inches apart, even if that wasn't the easiest place to make the hole. Usually, we screw in wherever it is most convenient, as long as the fitting is secure, but I told them that with the Trade Delegation contract, there were to be no deviations. Nine inches meant nine inches, and every hole had to be drilled, plugged and screwed, as though they were sitting their City and Guilds. This kind of work-to-rule would virtually double the time spent in each room. On a strictly commercial contract, I could never have carried the extra man hours, but Jay had already promised to subsidise any cost over-runs, and what we were trying to buy was time. The Russians were going to have the most stylishly double-glazed windows in the western hemisphere – I just hoped they never found out why!

When I had given the fitters their instructions, I sat down on the bed, which was covered with a dust-sheet. Marat, who had been watching and listening closely, sat down also, and we began a little conversation, consisting of the usual exchanges between strangers.

He knew my name already and he asked me where I came from. He seemed interested in my Irish background, but his questioning was very casual: there was no feeling that I was being interrogated.

I asked him how he liked London and his answer gave me my first surprise. He told me he had arrived in England only a few days previously; this was his first assignment and he had barely set foot outside the Trade Delegation. I thought for a moment they had brought a special security team over from Moscow to guard us, but Marat told me he was a timber expert. I laughed and said didn't they have enough forests for him to cut down in Russia. He smiled and explained that he was a timber marketing man, not a logger, and I gathered gradually that jobs like this escort duty were divided up among the commercial and administrative staff, and were most likely to fall to newcomers.

At least, that was Marat's version. I assumed automatically that he might well be KGB, and I even made a joke about it at one point. We were talking about my role on the site and I said I was there to supervise my men, while he supervised me. 'Just as long as the KGB doesn't get involved, we'll be fine,' I said.

I laughed as I said it and he took the joke in good part. I was treating Marat like any new client, starting with a bit of banter just to test his mood. Usually, a joke or two never goes amiss and anyway, it always helps to know whether the person you are dealing with has a sense of humour.

Marat laughed and said 'There's nothing like that to worry about,' and I said, more seriously, that I would answer for my men's honesty and general behaviour.

We chatted on and I was relieved to see that he was a heavy smoker, as I am myself. I gave him an English cigarette and he gave me a Russian one. It was rather strong and as I couldn't read the brand name, I asked Marat to pronounce it for me and was told they were Pyphoos. He asked me what I thought about them. I said I liked them very much and, instantly, he got up and walked out of the room leaving me alone.

He wasn't away long, and when he came back he threw two packets of Pyphoos on the bed, as a gift for me. It was a nice gesture, though I didn't know Marat well enough to be sure whether it was done from friendship or for some calculating game of his own. In these situations I spend all my time being cautious and calculating, and part of that is to assume that everyone on the other side is the same.

By mid-morning we were getting on well and I asked if there was any chance of a cup of tea. I said my chaps didn't normally stop work during the morning, but I liked a little break.

'That's no problem,' Marat said. 'You can use the canteen.'

I thanked him, but pointed out that Mr Denushenko had emphasised that I mustn't go anywhere in the building alone.

Marat grinned. 'Don't worry about that,' he said. 'I am your guard and I like tea too.'

We went upstairs to the canteen and immediately Marat

found there was no milk and went off to get some, leaving me on my own. Then, not long afterwards, the other guards came in, with no sign of my men, so I assumed they must have been left to work unsupervised. For a first day, the signs were already promising. Marat didn't seem very committed to his job; he certainly wasn't working to the letter of his instructions but, better still, I had the real feeling that he wasn't interested in escort work at all and wasn't the type to take it seriously just because he had been ordered to.

When Marat came back, a couple of the other guards came over to join us and I gathered from the chat that, like him, they had only just arrived in England. They asked me about places to visit and asked particularly how to get to the West End, which they had obviously been told about. I got out a tube map and explained the colour codes, showing them how to head for an easy jumping-off point like Piccadilly.

The thought crossed my mind that any one of the group could have been an experienced KGB officer who had been in London for years and could have found Piccadilly blindfolded, but I played the game absolutely straight, taking their queries at face value and being as helpful and friendly as I could.

When we had finished our tea, I said I ought to be keeping an eye on my men, but Marat showed no sign of wanting to move. When I got up, he said: 'You know the way. If you want me, I'll be here,' took a paperback book out of his pocket, settled down comfortably with his legs across the arm of the chair and started to read, leaving me to go downstairs with the other guards.

I still could not be sure that it was not some kind of test, but in the days that followed, I began to understand that my biggest ally was the boredom of the guards. Watching someone double-glaze a window is not exactly a thrilling way to pass the time. Most of the guards, like Marat, were apparently not professional security officers but members of the Trade Delegation, assigned by rota to what they regarded as a thoroughly tedious chore. Most of them had just arrived and could not wait to get out into London and start their proper work.

As soon as I realised this, I was all in favour of exploiting it and starting to go beyond routine observations, but Jay insisted again and again on caution. In this early period, Jay had been busy also, organising the debriefings and arranging a safe house for our meetings, the place he always referred to as the 'shop'.

The 'shop' turned out to be a service flat in an anonymous mansion block not far from Great Portland Street tube station. There were two dozen similar blocks in the surrounding streets and the location had been chosen so that it was very easy to check on whether you were being followed before you entered the building.

It was on the fifth floor, a small studio flat which was equipped for sleeping but which had obviously not been lived in regularly. The bed was in the main room, on a curious-looking dais, more than two feet off the ground, and there was also a tiny kitchen and bathroom. I was told that I could use the flat whenever I liked and Jay suggested there might be times when I would be depressed or anxious or just generally in bad spirits and I might need a place to hide in mentally. I never did have to use it for that reason, but there were times when it was reassuring to know that a refuge did exist if the situation turned nasty.

Yet though I never actually slept there, the 'shop' was to become a central part of my life. I hadn't realised how regularly Jay had planned to have debriefings and I found myself going there three or more times a week, even when the information I had to pass on was only routine. I had an early hint too that the debriefings were being taken very seriously. Quite soon after I began work, Jay produced the promised album of photographs of everyone in the Trade Delegation and asked me to identify the guards who had been assigned to us. I checked very carefully and found none of them.

Jay grinned. 'I'd have been surprised if you had found any,' he said. 'This book is at least three weeks out of date, if not more. I've had to make special arrangements with the Home Office to get hold of the photos of the latest intake. I'll have them by the next debriefing.'

At first, I was irritated by being tested, but I accepted

36

grudgingly that to Jay I was a new man; he wasn't trying to trap me, but he had to find out for himself how good my observation was or whether I would make up an identification just to please my new masters.

'Oh and don't forget one thing, Bill,' said Jay, 'It's a cliché, but it's true. Don't be fooled by people's apparent rank and status. The cook may well be a KGB officer.'

I soon began to acquire a real respect for Jay. I learned about his experiences as field agent in Moscow only later. In the early stages, I was impressed mainly by his diligence and attention to detail.

If he promised to do something or to check something for me, he always did so. It increased my own confidence to know that he was not the kind of controller who would say something to make me feel better, then take no action at all once I was out of sight. My only worry was that he seemed to be trying to hold me on too tight a leash. 'You're the one in the front line, Bill,' he used to say. 'If anything goes wrong, it's you who bears the brunt. Take no chances. As much as we want the job done, we have to look after your welfare.'

One night, as I was walking home with Mike after a debriefing, I said, 'For God's sake tell Jay he doesn't have to keep saying that, will you?'

'Don't worry about it,' Mike said. 'It's only that he hasn't worked with you like I have. He just wants to make sure you don't do anything silly because you don't know Russian ways.'

I didn't grumble, and for the first week or so I played strictly by Jay's rules. I examined every room carefully, but I touched nothing. I memorised faces, got to know the Trade Delegation's routines, and in each room I checked on personal photographs and souvenirs and anything that would give a clue to the occupant's background.

The only thing I handled was a red-covered book, written in English, which seemed to be in every room, like a Gideon bible. I picked it up and glanced at it quite openly. I wasn't being watched but if I had been caught, I could have explained it away as simple curiosity. It turned out to be a very boring official guide to the Soviet Union, giving the State's version of such fascinating statistics as how many doctors and nurses there were per thousand of the Soviet population.

Then, one day, on my own initiative, I decided to take a document. There was almost no risk involved. The room was not occupied and a piece of paper had been left in an empty wardrobe. I don't read Russian, so I had no idea what it was, but it didn't look like anything anyone would miss, so I pocketed it and handed it over to Mike.

Neither of us expected much from it and I was pleasantly surprised a couple of days later to receive a compliment from Jay.

'That bit of paper you took from the wardrobe was very interesting,' he said. 'It was a list of dos and don'ts for Soviet citizens arriving in England. It gave us quite a few insights into the way they think. There was a list of places where they shouldn't go and types of people they shouldn't associate with. It's always nice to know when anyone is stepping out of line. Well done, Bill.'

I was encouraged and I felt sure I could go a stage further and take something a bit more interesting. The opportunity came when we were glazing one of the larger bedrooms downstairs. It was occupied by three men, aged around forty to fifty, who were almost never there, and it was very untidy, which suggested that they were not the kind of people to notice if their possessions were disturbed. The only unusual point I noticed was that they smoked two different brands of cigarette, of a kind I hadn't seen anywhere else in the hotel, but I was far more interested in a very tempting briefcase, left in one corner, which was open and bulging with papers which looked as though they had been stuffed in carelessly.

I reported the situation to Jay the same night and told him I was sure I could take a couple of documents out of the case without anyone noticing.

'And do what with them?' Jay asked.

'I could take in a camera and photograph them,' I said. 'It would only take a couple of minutes.'

I could see Jay was tempted but he was very much against the idea of taking in a camera.

'It's too big a risk,' he said. 'OK. They've been lax up to now, but they could easily insist on searching your toolbag, as part of a routine security check, and if anyone glimpsed you through the flat window using a camera, the whole operation would be over.'

'So why don't I nick a couple of documents,' I said. 'I could take them in the morning, have a long lunch hour, give them to Mike, and put them back in the afternoon.'

Jay was still doubtful but I could see that, like me, he wanted something tangible to show to his superiors. We went over the security situation yet again; how the guards behaved, how I could avoid being seen by my own men, what excuse I would make to get out of the Trade Delegation early. We didn't have to spend any time on the procedures for meeting Mike; they were already well-established. He had spent a happy ten days touring the pubs in Hampstead, Highgate and Kentish Town, drinking and lunching on expenses, picking out a series of suitable ones we could use in rotation. We had set up a system for me to telephone in advance when I wanted to make contact; Mike would be there automatically, and we had set routines for handing over information if I wanted to or ignoring each other, if that was appropriate.

Finally, Jay made a phone call about the briefcase and gave me the go-ahead.

'If the guards are as slack as you say, we may as well have a go,' he said.

And it went off without a hitch. I played my usual guessing-game, visiting the four rooms we were working on and making sure that, at the right moment, I was in the three-bed room and Marat was somewhere else. The brief-case was still there, untouched from the day before. I took out three documents from the middle of the bundle and slipped them into my jacket pocket. At 11 o'clock I explained to Marat that I had to go out to check on the supply of some materials. The fitters who overheard just grinned. They knew I was off for a quick pint.

The pub for that day was the Assembly Rooms in Kentish Town. I handed the documents over to Mike in the toilet; he left immediately, and I had a couple of quiet drinks alone at the bar, chatting to the landlord.

I was surprised myself at how little time Mike took. I

discovered later that he had not needed to go back to the office. MI6 had parked a van a few streets away with a xerox machine inside. By half-past three, the copies were in Jay's hands and the originals were back in the briefcase!

I didn't find out straightaway what had been learned from the documents, but on the next debriefing, Jay was really enthusiastic.

'The papers from the briefcase were terrific,' he said. 'We're following them up now. Those three are Hungarians. The documents were in Hungarian - and those were Hungarian cigarettes by the way, if you should spot them again. I'll keep you posted.'

True to form with Jay, it was some time before I got the whole story. Often Jay told me only a few fragments of what they were doing as a result of my activities, and sometimes he told me nothing at all. This time, though, I could see Jay wanted to encourage me and keep up my enthusiasm and he gave me more than usual.

The documents had been significant enough for Jay to use foot patrols to establish individual surveillance on the three Hungarians in the room. I took no part in these investigations, except to warn Jay that I had seen at least one of the three leaving the Trade Delegation by the side entrance and setting off over Hampstead Heath.

The suspicions aroused by the documents had been confirmed immediately as the three wandered around London wearing entirely different styles of dress depending on where they were going. The common thread though was that they were mingling in different milieux within the Hungarian exile community – and pretending to be exiles themselves who had escaped to Britain after the uprising.

Many of the exiles were now prosperous businessmen, and Jay's people had learned that the Trade Delegation Hungarians were identifying those who were contributing funds to be fed back to the underground organisations inside Hungary.

As a result of the enquiries, a number of leading Hungarian businessmen were warned, in time, that some of their 'friends' were untrustworthy, and what had begun with the casual theft of a couple of pieces of paper turned into a nice little intelligence success.

I was delighted when I was told, but by the time I found out the details I was already nicely dug in at the Trade Delegation and progressing well with even more intriguing lines of inquiry.

CHAPTER 4

In the weeks that followed I had more successes and also failures, and the trouble was that I had no real way of determining which would become which. As I moved from room to room, I observed everything I could, kept notes, and reported to Jay, but when I came across something which looked like a promising lead, whether or not I could follow it up was usually a matter of chance. I would spot something in one room which intrigued Jay but I would be unable to examine it closely, either because one of the Soviet guards was there or because one of my own men was staring through a window from a ladder outside. Then, by the next day, the item would be gone, the double-glazing finished and I would have no reason to return to that particular room. It was a tantalising process but I learned to make the most of the tiniest opportunity and the detailed probings during Jay's debriefings helped to ensure that nothing, however small, was overlooked.

Sometimes, though, I was just plain lucky. One day, for instance, I was on the second floor of the hotel when I saw two Chinese men walking towards me down the corridor. Strictly speaking I should say Chinese-looking men because they turned out to be Mongolians, but I have to admit that my knowledge of the Soviet Asian republics is a bit vague. I was interested precisely because of my ignorance; I didn't realise they were from the Soviet Union and I was curious to know what Chinese were doing in the Soviet Trade Delegation.

As it happened, my ignorance provided a fascinating lead. I reported to Jay simply that I had seen these two men in the hotel. I didn't know which room they occupied but I was able to watch them go down the stairs, out of the hotel, and through the side gate of the complex, out onto Hampstead Heath. As it was a fairly quiet period, Jay decided to have them followed and their movements gave a completely fresh insight into Soviet intelligence activities in London.

Like the Hungarians, these 'Chinese' were interested in the exile community. They were, in fact passing themselves off as Chinese and mingling in the cafés, restaurants and shops of London's Chinatown but observation over a period showed that they were doing far more than circulating to pick up casual gossip. To the Chinese community, they appeared to have legitimate business interests which gave them an entrée into the fraternity of traders and international merchants who maintained links with Hong Kong, and through Hong Kong with mainland China.

They were engaged in very sophisticated economic intelligence-gathering, focused on the movement of money and trading plans in Hong Kong for the period leading up to the territory's return to Chinese sovereignty. All of this took a while to establish, of course, and I took no part in the investigation. My contribution was to tip Jay off after the chance meeting in the corridor of the hotel, but without that, the investigation would never have started since once the two men passed outside the gates of the Trade Delegation, no one, including their business contacts in the environs of Gerrard Street, had any idea of their Soviet origins.

It was a nice little success, but at the other end of the scale, what looked like one of the most promising leads during my whole period in the hotel petered out infuriatingly. I was clearing up one evening after my men had finished work in the canteen. The guards had dispersed and, as was happening more and more frequently, Marat had gone off somewhere leaving me completely alone. In one corner of the canteen was a map which had slid off a table and was lying, half open, on the floor. I took a quick look and saw that it was an Ordnance Survey map of the Central Highlands of Scotland. There were several red rings marked on it, circling tiny places which were well off any route likely to be taken by even the most adventurous tourist and which seemed too far apart to be stages of a walking holiday. I quickly jotted down the place names and the map references and put the map back where it had been lying, presumably after being dropped

43

during a meeting in the canteen. I gave the names to Jay and at a later debriefing, he ordered me to do everything I possibly could to find out who had left the map in the canteen. The red circles marked the locations of radar stations in the DEW line, the Distant Early Warning system, against nuclear attacks. Someone in the Trade Delegation was closely interested, but who? I simply had to find out.

The greatest frustration of my work was that I could never ask questions. I dare not risk even a roundabout query because, however subtly I introduced it, it would have seemed out of character. To the Russians, I was a friendly Irish workman who liked a drink and a chat about football and throughout the entire period of the contract I never stepped out of that character, even for a moment.

I never once dropped my guard and I never underestimated Marat either. He could have been playing exactly the same game. Every time he appeared to be reading his book, he could have been paying attention to everything I was doing or saying. I played along with his apparently casual attitude and always tried to seem relaxed, but I never really relaxed, ever.

On the question of the map, I was completely stymied. I wasn't able to hang around the canteen to see if anyone came back for it because it was time for me to knock off and leave the complex, and I dare not ask anyone who had been sitting in that particular corner. Jay alerted the security people at the radar stations, but as far as I know, nothing was ever discovered.

I had another disappointment when I thought that a bottle of vodka was nicely loosening the tongue of one of the guards. It was a bitterly cold winter's day, too cold for the men to be working safely on outside ladders. Glass and aluminium are both very cold to the touch and it is quite possible for a man's hand to freeze on the surface so that it goes numb and he cannot feel the weight or shape of the window he is holding. I called a break on safety grounds and the chaps went gratefully indoors and settled down in the canteen, and the guards were delighted to go with them.

I went upstairs with Marat and we chose a table in the

corner of the canteen. The room was almost dark. The evening was already drawing in and the only light in the canteen was from the television set. We were joined by another member of the escort detail, a young man called Alexis, whom I was especially interested in because he had already struck me as the most naive of the people assigned to us.

Right from the first week, one of the activities of the guards which had amused and irritated us in turn was their habit of quizzing us about English slang. I know it sounds ridiculous but it is literally true that whenever one of my men or I said anything that was not absolutely standard English, someone would write it down. When I got to know Marat better I made a comment about it. He laughed it off, saying that all newcomers were under instructions to improve their knowledge of English, from a practical, everyday standpoint. I never did establish whether it was just that or whether all the data the guards were collecting was being fed into some giant computer in Moscow to help train intelligence officers for their future undercover work. If it was, then my men contributed a hilarious mixture of cockney rhyming slang and Irish dialect, not to mention a few blistering oaths when they got their fingers jammed in a window frame. The point about Alexis was that he was the most enthusiastic – and the most obvious – about carrying out his instructions. The others at least tried to be discreet about it, but with Alexis, you could hardly get through a sentence without him whipping out a pad, and he must have filled two whole notebooks with 'jottings from the ladders'.

I asked Marat about him and learned that he was the only member of the team of guards who was not a Muscovite. Marat said he came from Murmansk, which I knew was a big Soviet naval base, and he was an expert in drawing plans. When I asked what sort of plans, Marat shrugged and said 'Oh, architectural ... that sort of thing.'

When he came to join us in the canteen, Alexis asked Marat and me if we would like some tea. I winked and asked if there was any chance of anything stronger.

Alexis grinned. 'You like a drink, do you, Bill?'

'Yes. I like my lunch-time pint,' I said, 'but I was thinking of some of your nice Russian vodka.'

'That's easy,' Alexis said. 'I will be back.'

He went away, and when he returned he slipped a full bottle of vodka out of his coat and we settled down to a nice session in the half darkness.

As we chatted, I could see that Alexis was becoming very relaxed and loose, and I could also see that Marat was growing nervous, as though he knew the younger man wasn't good at holding his drink and might say something he shouldn't. I kept drinking fast and encouraged Alexis to stay level as I was sure I could get him to be indiscreet if we went on long enough. Finally he said – of all things, 'Bill, have any flying saucers been seen in England?'

I'm afraid flying saucers are not something I take very seriously. Marat looked worried by the remark but I presumed it was because he didn't like Alexis to make an ass of himself. I reported the whole conversation to Jay who told me to keep an ear open for any follow-up as extra-terrestial and para-normal phenomena were taken seriously in the Soviet Union, but nothing came of it and I felt that a nice opportunity with vodka loosening Alexis' tongue had been wasted.

In this catalogue of disappointments, I had better also include Martia, the hotel supervisor. I came to know her well over the weeks, and we also double-glazed her personal room, which gave me some insight into her family life. She had a son with her, a boy of about fourteen, who, unlike many other children I met during the course of the work, seemed rather surly and bad-tempered towards me. When I was in the room, he barely spoke to me and spent most of his time staring out of the window at the squirrels playing in the trees. There was no man living with Martia but I could not establish whether she was widowed or whether her husband was just not in England.

Jay was interested in Martia because he thought he recognised in her the kind of woman the KGB frequently uses to spy on their own people. During the conversations about Martia, I gathered that Jay had been in Moscow several times and had had at least one extended tour of duty there. He said it was standard practice for Soviet intelligence to use an attractive, unattached, middle-aged woman like Martia to act as a magnet for the lonely men in the Trade Delegation. 'Maybe the son doesn't like men because he sees too many of them,' Jay said.

At his suggestion, I made a point of watching as closely as I could the comings and goings around her room, but this line of inquiry led nowhere. Occasionally, when I made some excuse to go to her room in the morning, I would find the dirty glasses and leftovers from a small party, and later I discovered she did have a lover – a man who worked in the administration block and who came over and spent the occasional hour or two with her during the day. Nothing, however, supported Jay's theory that she might be linked with the security of the Trade Delegation.

These disappointments, though, seem very minor in retrospect, compared with what we did manage to achieve, but I had to be patient. The difference between this kind of operation and an ordinary intelligence investigation is that you have to wait for leads to present themselves; you can't make the running. I was in the building day in and day out, watching and recording, but the double-glazing work dictated where I could or could not be.

As the weeks passed, I acquired a free run in certain limited areas: I could go to the canteen alone, or go to seek out Martia, and if I went over to look for Mr Denushenko, no one bothered to come with me, so I could often check car numbers and watch people entering and leaving the complex. What I could not do was to go into parts of the building without a clear pretext. This meant that often I would see someone in the hotel who interested me, follow them into the grounds, then be forced to let them vanish into the admin. block of flats – which I came on to later – or risk arousing suspicion.

Fortunately, I did get lucky more than once, and one such chance break started Jay off on inquiries which were to have far-reaching implications. I walked into the canteen late one lunch-time and spotted a man I had not seen before who interested me from the very first sight. Two things struck me about him straightaway: his dress and his general ease of manner.

He was under thirty but was more smartly dressed than anyone I had seen in the Trade Delegation, including the Hungarian trio. He was wearing a superbly cut blue City suit, with a cotton shirt and a discreet tie, and he could easily have been a rich young stockbroker or investment analyst. He was sitting sprawled in an arm chair, with his legs over the arm, his tie loosened and his shirt unbuttoned, chatting to a young woman and another man of his own age. They had obviously been drinking, and though they weren't exactly staggering about, it was clear they had come from a very enjoyable and very liquid lunch. In the context of the general bearing of the people in the Trade Delegation, it was astonishing that such a young man should make no attempt to conceal that he had been drinking during the day. I already knew that plenty of people in the Trade Delegation liked a drink, but Denushenko appeared to enforce strictly the rule that no alcohol was to be consumed in working hours. When the guards were drinking with me, they were extremely discreet about it, in fact it was obvious that even quite senior people had to sneak a drink if they wanted one during the day. This young man, in contrast, was completely at ease. He clearly felt that he had the right to have been wherever he had been, which – combined with the elegant clothes and languid manner – made him very intriguing.

I would have watched for him again closely anyway, but my interest was really sharpened when I saw him a few days later, dressed entirely differently.

He was wearing a suit again, but this time the City gent image had been replaced by snazzy East End flash. The suit was wide-striped and loud and he also wore a trilby and a coloured shirt. He would have looked perfectly in place selling used cars from a lot in Bow or Whitechapel. After that, I manoeuvred as best I could to be in places where I might catch a glimpse of him, and Jay organised close individual surveillance on him whenever they could pick him up outside the complex.

48

This time, the results did not disappoint. Inside the delegation I saw him four or five times. On each occasion, he was dressed differently – once in his City pinstripes again, and at other times in rich men's leisure clothes, with a smart golfing blouson and slacks, and once as though he was going to run a market barrow.

Outside the complex, Jay's people had trailed him all over London. His main haunt was the City, where he behaved exactly like any other ambitious young man, anxious to rise in financial circles. He was trailed to the Stock Exchange, to Lloyds and to various brokerage houses, and though he never actually did any work, he was very skilled in giving the appearance that he was. He had friends everywhere. He lunched and drank in dive bars, attended private luncheon parties with City people and generally moved within the financial community without seeming at all conspicuous. He also spent time socialising in Hampstead and Highgate, and went as far afield as Soho and to some pubs in South London frequented by heavyweight villains.

'Our best guess is that he is a trainee intelligence officer,' said Jay. 'We've come across the type before and his behaviour fits exactly. He's here on a three month visa and he'll probably move on to Washington or one of their European embassies, depending on his languages. Judging by his age, I'd say he was just starting out on a KGB career, digging himself in and making himself at ease with the Western way of life.

'What we want to know most,' Jay went on, 'is who his contacts are in London. Who he sees. Who he reports to in the Trade Delegation. I know it's tricky, but do your best. We really want to know about this man.'

We ended the debriefing on an optimistic note but both Jay and I knew that I might well not get any further. I hadn't seen the young man again nor the woman who had been with him on the first occasion, and when I had glimpsed him walking through the Delegation, he had always been alone.

Then, by pure chance, his room came up for double-glazing! When we started it, I didn't even know it was his, but I didn't have any doubt when I took a look around and found his whole collection of clothes in a wardrobe – East End, West End, City and low life, everything from cheese-cutters to old school ties.

More important still, I found a diary, or more accurately, I spotted one on a desk, but before I could do anything with it, one of my chaps came into the room.

I arranged an emergency meeting with Jay and his reaction was predictable: 'Get the diary at all costs.'

I couldn't steal it – we agreed that was too much of a risk – and I couldn't read it, but I did manage to get my hands on it, and my luck held beyond any possible expectation. The address section of the diary was written mostly in English and there were three pages of London telephone numbers, as well as the extensions of the people he needed to call in the embassy in Kensington.

I grabbed a workman's pad and copied everything I could understand: addresses, numbers, and entries in the diary itself, wherever I could make sense of them. I had arranged the work so that my men were in a different room and I had the diary in my hands for the best part of half an hour.

I got the material to Mike the same day and at the next debriefing, Jay was more jubilant than I had ever seen him.

'We've been working on the diary, Bill,' he said. 'This time, you've hit the jackpot.'

CHAPTER 5

One of the names which figured regularly in the diary was Captain Anatoli Pavlovich Zotov, the Soviet naval attaché at the embassy in Kensington who was expelled from Britain for spying in December 1982.

At the time of the expulsion – for 'activities incompatible with his diplomatic status' – there were leaks to the press that Zotov had tried to set up a spy ring in Britain. Later, when the British naval attaché in Moscow, Captain Bruce Richardson, was sent home in a tit-for-tat expulsion, there were more stories in the press, this time suggesting that Zotov had been expelled because British intelligence had over-reacted. The naval attaché had been accused of trying to recruit spies while on visits to Portsmouth and Torquay, and the new stories hinted that all that had really happened was that Zotov had behaved a bit indiscreetly by buying drinks for people in a seaside pub.

The British authorities chose, for their own reasons, not to leak the truth about what Zotov had been up to, possibly so as not to give the impression that he had damaged Britain's national security. I don't know myself what damage, if any, Zotov did, but I do know for certain that he had a damned good try.

Before his name appeared in the diary, I had already sighted Zotov in the Trade Delegation and Jay had been immediately interested when I reported it. I could hardly have missed his arrival at Highgate as he came in naval uniform, a rare sight in the Delegation. He was chauffeur-driven in a limousine which dropped him at the main entrance and parked there, instead of going into the special parking area, which was most unusual even for VIP vehicles. Both Denushenko and Bartov came out onto the steps to greet him and they had one of those little chats which you can recognise instantly as a meeting between very senior people – the kind when no matter how many people are actually there, only certain ones are considered present and all the rest are psychologically excluded.

When I identified him from the album of photographs of staff at the Kensington embassy, Jay was curious to know why he had appeared at the Trade Delegation. There were occasional social contacts, Jay said, but generally the embassy and Trade Delegation people kept well apart, as if to underline the firm distinction Moscow always drew between trade and policital relations.

'Even when a crisis blows up and we're on the verge of breaking off diplomatic relations, trade always goes quietly on,' Jay said. 'That's their way, and I supose you have to say it's our way too, as we go along with it.'

I did not see Zotov again at Highgate but Jay gave me plenty of details about him later which made nonsense of the press stories suggesting that his expulsion had been a mistake. One evening, while we were having a drink to unwind after a debriefing, Jay told me about one of Zotov's trips to Portsmouth which the press did not get to hear about.

Zotov was already marked for making unscheduled and unauthorised trips outside London and was subjected to regular personal surveillance. One morning, he was picked up leaving the embassy with another Russian and followed to Victoria. They went into the station hotel, stayed there briefly, then Zotov came out alone, walked over to the booking office and bought a ticket for a South coast resort.

Because he was already a key target, they had a double surveillance team on him, which was just as well since he got off the train after a couple of stops, returned to Victoria, took a taxi across to Waterloo and caught a train there for Portsmouth.

Believing he had shaken any possible tail, Zotov then began a little escapade which confirmed beyond any doubt that he had far overstepped the bounds of the duties of an attaché. He spent two days in a hotel in old Portsmouth, poked around the restricted naval area and at one point he was photographed collecting water samples on the edge of the

52

submarine base, presumably for analysis to check the type of submarine fuel that was being used.

The diary I had copied showed that the trainee intelligence officer kept in regular touch with Zotov. Another of the trainee's contacts was a man MI6 referred to as 'the Professor'. He was another Kensington official who spent much of his time travelling to Oxford where he had established himself as a don, without disclosing his Soviet connections, and was doing research in the university libraries into aircraft specifications. Although his excursions to Oxford were un-authorised, he was not technically engaged in intelligence activities but merely in gathering of the kind of published information which is available to anyone who knows where to look.

The same could not be said, however, of the man referred to as 'the Major' who became my biggest coup in the first three months inside the Trade Delegation. Any doubts I might have had about the extent of Societ intelligence activities in London had long since been dispelled both by my own observations inside the complex and by the debriefing sessions with Jay. The list of people I already knew to be engaged in 'activities incompatible with diplomatic status' was already impressive: the Hungarian trio, the 'Chinese', the pinstriped trainee, the Professor, Zotov – not to mention the unknown owner of the map of the Scottish radar installations – but the Major was in a class of his own.

As usual, I saw him first by chance. He was walking along a second floor corridor in the hotel and of all the Russians I had seen so far, he was without question the one who looked most like an Englishman.

He was a man in his mid-forties, stockily built with a clipped moustache, dressed in a British Warm military topcoat and cavalry twill trousers, and carrying a cane-handled umbrella, tightly rolled in the best Whitehall tradi-tion. His hair, though receding, was well cut and tidily groomed and he had an unmistakeable air of distinction about him; he walked with the confidence of true British army bearing, not at all like a foreigner playing the part.

I couldn't turn about and follow him without being

conspicuous, but as he was dressed for going out, I assumed he was leaving the building, so I let him get downstairs, then I hung about by the window at the end of the corridor to try and see which way he was going out. Usually, all I would have learned was whether he used the main entrance, or the side gate, but in the past that had been useful in helping Jay's foot patrols to pick up someone as they left the complex.

This time, there was a most unusual development that I had not anticipated at all. Parked outside the main gate, as it was every morning, was the bus which took the children to the Russian school. Its departure was one of the Trade Delegation's unchanging rituals; the children assembled at the gate and were counted onto the bus; every evening they returned and were counted back off. Apart from the driver, no adults travelled on the bus, but as I watched from the upstairs window, I could see quite clearly that the figure in the British Warm was getting in with the children.

I rushed downstairs to make sure and stood by the main entrance, as nonchalantly as I could, scanning the bus, but I could no longer see him. I knew I hadn't been mistaken – he had got on, but now I could see rows of seats on both sides of the vehicle, most of the children had settled down, and the man was nowhere to be seen. The only possible conclusion was that he had boarded the bus and was deliberately hiding!

I have to admit that despite all my professional training, I was so excited I could barely wait to report to Jay at the next debriefing. Jay listened and I sensed that he was troubled but he made no comment; even when I tried to arouse his enthusiasm, he simply produced the album of photographs and watched me go through it, page by page. The man was so unlike anyone else I had seen at the Trade Delegation that I knew he would not be hard to pick out, but his photograph was not in the book. We tried the embassy album and again he was not there. Jay insisted that I go over both books and second and third time, but I knew there was no point. If his photo had been there, I would have identified it straightaway.

I could tell from Jay's reaction that he did not like the situation at all, but he would not explain. All he said was 'I think I'd better dig out some older photographs, just in case.'

The urgency was obvious however as he insisted on a meeting the following night, even though there was no debriefing scheduled.

As soon as I arrived, Jay produced a set of loose photographs and scattered them across the little coffee table. 'These are from files that are no longer current,' he said. 'Let's see if you can find your man there.'

It took me about five seconds and I could tell that Jay was not surprised.

'Christ, Bill, I hope you're wrong,' he said, but there was no conviction in his voice. He knew I was right and I knew something was seriously amiss.

I tried to get Jay to tell me what was going on, but it was almost a week before he raised the issue again. Mike called my brother-in-law at the factory to arrange an urgent meeting with me at the Assembly Rooms pub in Kentish Town. When I arrived Mike was already there, and he did not even finish his drink or offer me one. We went straight out to Mike's car and he drove me over to the 'shop' for a meeting with Jay. When we got there, Jay asked Mike if he would mind waiting in the pub down the road and I knew from his tone that he was not at all his usual relaxed self.

'Bill,' he said, when we were alone, 'what we talk about tonight is between us. Nothing must be said to Mike at all.' I said I didn't like that idea. 'If Mike has done something wrong, I'd like to know about it,' I protested. 'Mike's a first class man and from my side of things, he's been doing a great job.'

'I know he has,' Jay said, 'This has nothing to do with Mike personally. It has to do with our relations with Special Branch. The man you spotted – the military-looking man, frankly he's an embarrassment to our service. We have quite a bit of egg on our faces over him and it's not something we want Special Branch involved in.'

Gradually, over several glasses of scotch, Jay told me the full story. The man in the British Warm was well known to MI6, who referred to him as the Major. He was a senior KGB officer who had operated in Britain four years previously and had been one of their most effective agents. He had

55

carried out espionage operations himself and he had re-cruited contacts and informants as well, building up a very worrying network. He specialised in the surveillance of military installations and one of his strong points then had been his ability to slip outside the diplomatic world and range widely around Britain without being detected. He had be-come a considerable embarrassment and MI6 had organised an operation to get rid of him; the end result was supposed to have been a situation in which he was forced to leave Britain and go back to Moscow, but avoiding the problems of formal expulsion, which always carries the risk of counter-measures against Britons in the Soviet Union.

'He did leave,' Jay said, 'but to be honest, we had no idea he was back, or when he came. He's managed to slip through the Home Office net as well as ours, and Christ knows what he's up to. It doesn't make us look too clever. He's a dangerous man and now that you've spotted him, we'll deal with him again, but you can see it's not a situation we want to have widely known about in the other services.'

Inter-service rivalry was something I understood well enough, and I could just imagine what had been going on behind the scenes since I had identified him. I was glad anyway that Mike wasn't being cut out because of something he was supposed to have done, and I persuaded Jay to agree to let me tell Mike, in strict confidence, a bit about what was happening. I didn't want one of my closest friends believing he had been frozen out without good reason, and Jay finally accepted that.

'From now on, Bill,' Jay said, 'the Major is your main target. Find out who he sees if you can, and most all, try and find out which is his room.'

I agreed, but I was faced with the old familiar problem: I had to rely largely on chance. In theory, I would come to his room eventually as I had seen him coming from the part of the hotel we had not yet double-glazed, but even if I found out which was his room, I dare not risk changing the work schedule to get into his place early. There was also the possibility that I might get to his room and finish it without ever knowing he was the occupant.

56

As it turned out, I need not have worried: it was Denu-shenko himself who inadvertently signalled that we were coming to 'the big one'.

As I was preparing my work schedule one morning, I discovered that the key for one of the next block of rooms was missing from the downstairs board. I asked Martia and she referred me to Denushenko who said, 'When you do this room, the guard will keep the key. He will unlock it for you and lock it up again when you leave.'

I felt sure this was going to be the Major's room. I could not be absolutely certain, but it was in the right part of the hotel and it seemed too much of a coincidence that there should be two high security rooms just in that section. Jay, meanwhile, had started virtually round-the-clock surveillance on the Major while he was out and about in London but it was only much later that he told me what he discovered.

I did not have to wait that long, though, to find out for myself that we were dealing with someone very special: the room – and it did turn out to be his – told me that from the moment I walked through the door.

It was as though the Major had created his own private flat in the middle of the hotel; a little enclave of luxury and comfort which far exceeded anything I had seen anywhere else in the complex. The room was lined with books, not the kind of cheap paperbacks there were in the other rooms, but properly bound hardbacks, many of them in English, on subjects ranging from aeronautics to computers, as well as history and politics and a lot of current novels. The bed had been covered over, but when I adjusted the dust sheet, I saw it had silk sheets and pillow slips, and the rest of the furniture was in keeping. Elsewhere in the room there was every kind of creature comfort, including an expensive music centre and a set of classical records. There were high quality teas, Havana cigars and boxes of chocolates, not to mention a drinks table stocked with spirits and liqueurs. It was the room of a man who had taste, and who didn't want for anything.

Luckily it was also a much bigger room than the others – it had been made by knocking three standard rooms together on a corner – and it had five windows to double-glaze which meant I spent a week there altogether.

I needed all of that, especially when I found under one of the dustsheets, a very complicated radio receiver and transmitter. I can still remember vividly the problems I had with Jay over that radio equipment. I don't know very much about electronics, but Jay wanted every detail and I never had time to study it in peace and quiet because with all the exposed windows, I was constantly in danger of being seen either by Marat, or by one of my own men.

Jay held a debriefing every night for a week and each time he grilled me until I dreamed about that radio equipment. He made me draw the dials and the layout and the next night he would make me draw bits of it again if he thought I hadn't got some detail quite right. On one point, though, I did manage to satisfy him: when my men took out the big window, it exposed the aerial lead which I was able to trace as far as the tree outside the window. When I drew the aerial layout for Jay he said, 'Right, I think we'd better take a look ourselves. Don't be surprised if you see a bit of activity overhead tomorrow.'

The next day a private commercial helicopter flew over in the morning and I just smiled and went on working, but I was very surprised when the same machine flew over nearly twenty times in the course of the day.

'You were a bit obvious, weren't you,' I said to Jay at the next debriefing.

'It was worth it,' he replied. 'Take a look at these.'

The photographs he showed me were so close and sharp they could have been taken from my workmen's ladders. One of them showed the tree with the detail of the aerial picked out against the bark and another one you could see right inside the room, with the head of one of my chaps in silhouette against the window frame.

'That transmitter he's got is better than the official one for the Trade Delegation,' Jay said, 'and as a matter of interest he doesn't transmit to Moscow. His signals are relayed via another of their embassies in Western Europe.'

Jay didn't say which and I didn't bother asking because I knew he would have told me if he had intended me to know.

58

But much later – almost ten weeks from the day when I first saw the Major getting into the school bus – Jay did tell me what the foot surveillance had turned up.

'Our major is quite an operator,' he said one night, when we had finished a debriefing. 'Would you like to hear about his caravan?'

I said I certainly would and from the relaxed way Jay told me the story, I gathered both that he had sorted out whatever embarrassment there had been over the Major's return to Britain and that he was on top of the situation again.

The reason I saw so little of the Major in the Trade Delegation, I later learned, was that he lived for long stretches at a time in a luxurious caravan in, of all places, Surrey. The caravan was parked in a pleasant rural setting on a farm, to allow the Major to indulge his interest in wildlife. It also happened to be near an ultra-sensitive military installation. The Major spent so much of his time there that he was accepted quite naturally as part of the local community. He drank in the same pubs as the personnel from the base and he was friendly and liked by everyone, especially as he was always quick to buy his round. No one knew anything about his Russian background. He was simply accepted as an ex-officer type, a decent sort of chap who enjoyed natural history and country life. In short, the Major was up to his old tricks again, using his ability to pass himself off as a seemingly reliable, yet harmless, military type, in order to collect information at military installations, both by observation and by gaining the confidence of base employees, who thought him the sort of patriotic Englishman in whom there was no risk involved in confiding.

The Major was never expelled. He was forced – for the second time – to leave unofficially, to avoid a tit-for-tat expulsion and, I suspect, to avoid any risk of exposing Jay's earlier embarrassment.

I did have the satisfaction though of seeing Zotov expelled and later, another Trade Delegation official, Vassily Ionov, who was also mentioned in the trainee's diary.

I can see the sense of not having too many expulsions; the intelligence services on both sides understand how the game is played, but for someone like me, who works on the fringe of the intelligence community, it is sometimes a bit disappointing.

I like to see the results of my work and I can tell you there is nothing in the world more satisfying than turning on the television and watching a 'target' you have been involved with going through his embarrassed farewells and protestations of innocence at Heathrow as he heads back to Moscow.

My kind of intelligence work can be very satisfying because you can achieve long-term results, without violence. Intelligence-gathering will always go on, I recognise that; but it is vital that it should be kept within bounds, and part of my role is to be able to administer a salutary little shock now and again to the Russians to show them that they cannot get away with much on British soil. I wouldn't want to labour the point, because it is not in my nature to make a song and dance about patriotism, but I believe very strongly in my country. I like to feel that I am doing my share to protect British freedom and the British way of life.

Watching a Soviet spy being forced to go back home, his tail between his legs, because he has been caught out by your own efforts, is like winning the pools. You can't tell anyone – not even your own wife, but it is still a great feeling. You watch and you say to yourself, 'I had a hand in that – and the poor sucker doesn't even realise how he was had!'

CHAPTER 6

'Tell me, Bill,' Jay said, 'how much do you know about bugging?' I grinned. We had come a long way in just a few months from the days of 'Now, don't take any risks whatever, Bill,' and 'Remember, this is strictly an observation job'. I had been expecting the question: it was the obvious next step and, as Jay well knew, I was ready for it.

As he always did, Jay picked exactly the right psychological moment to ask the question. I was feeling exceptionally confident because I had just managed to turn around what had looked like a very depressing situation when we had begun the second stage of the double-glazing contract.

It took nearly three months to double-glaze the hotel section of the complex and by the end of it, I was well dug in. I had become a familiar figure in the Trade Delegation and while I avoided going anywhere unusual, no one ever questioned my movements. The system of working on four rooms at a time provided me with countless opportunities to spend a few minutes – and often a lot longer – alone, here and there, and I became extremely adept at removing documents, letters and small items from the various rooms. Hardly a day passed in which I did not find something to interest Jay, in addition to the growing list of notable intelligence successes.

When we finished the hotel, I was riding high, but at first sight it looked as though the next stage was going to be a terrible anti-climax. Professionally speaking – as head of a double-glazing company that is! – the early work had gone well. Denushenko and his superiors were well satisfied with the windows and doors we had fitted and there was no problem in re-negotiating a further contract for many thousands of pounds. The drawback, viewed from the intelligence angle, was that the Russians wanted us to work next on the assembly hall and the library area. It was a huge job and it was a large, open area, where I saw little prospect of being able to keep out of sight of watching eyes.

The assembly hall was the heart of the Trade Delegation. It was used for everything from dances and banquets to lectures and political meetings. It served as ballroom and conference centre, but during the day, when it was generally not in use, it was simply a big, bare room, with rows of empty chairs. In an adjacent room, there was a snooker-like table for playing Russian billiards, and a large library area, with shelves of books which included English classic authors from Shakespeare to Dickens, and copies of newspapers from all over the Soviet Union, bound in large unwieldy volumes which could not be taken apart for reading.

The basic problem was that there was nowhere for me to sneak about in! No nooks and crannies; no odd corners where I could slip out of sight for a moment to copy down something that had caught my attention. Worse still, the situation might last for months. The hall, library and billiard room, together with an adjoining children's recreation area, had high windows and broad patio doors. Even if I modified the 'work-to-rule' policy and tried to speed things up, I estimated that I might be in the area for up to six months, during which time I risked achieving very little for Jay.

I set to work gloomily, believing I might lose all the momentum we had built up, but I soon discovered that one factor was working in my favour: the guards also seemed to have decided that there was no need to be vigilant in such an open area. Marat and his colleagues were already bored beyond description with the chore of supervising us. A few new faces had joined the escort group but essentially they were the same crew who had been with us for three months and they were obviously heartily sick of double-glazing in all its forms! Once we moved into the assembly hall and library area, they more or less dropped all pretence at supervising us individually. While my men went up and down ladders and shuffled back and forth carrying windows and doors, the guards would settle down in the library or recreation area, reading, watching television, or playing chess or billiards.

That aspect was encouraging but I still had the problem of

finding something in the area worth examining. Then, one morning, I noticed the group photographs.

I was standing beside the long wall in the leisure area and, out of boredom, I began examining the notice board. I had gone over it before but most of the notices were in Russian and anyway I would not have expected to obtain much intelligence material from a public notice board. This time, I started examining more closely a series of photographs in a glass wall cabinet which had obviously been taken at a big formal function. There were seven or eight photographs in all, showing different angles of a banquet in the assembly hall; some of the photos were overall views of the scene, while others were shot of individual tables. Everyone was either in uniform or formal clothes and it looked as though the event had been the high point of the Trade Delegation year.

I recognised Denushenko, Bartov, Marat and Alexis and many other people I had come to know either personally or by sight during the first three months.

The person who really caught my attention however was a man whose name I learned later was Gariachi. He was to play a big role in a later part of the operation, but up to that point he was someone I had been aware of only as a figure moving around the grounds of the complex. Several times I had seen him in rough workman's clothing, sweeping up leaves on the lawns at the front of the complex. At other times I had seen him in chauffeur's uniform, polishing the big black limousine which was used to carry VIPs to and from Heathrow and into London. I had noticed Gariachi mainly because whenever I saw him cleaning the car, I knew we could expect the possible arrival of a dignitary who might interest Jay, but I was struck by the fact that in the photographs he was sitting at the top table, right between Denushenko and Bartov. At the same table there was Captain Zotov, the naval attaché from the embassy in Kensington, and several other people who were clearly high in the Soviet pecking order in London. If I had learned nothing else during my months in the Trade Delegation, it was that the Soviet Union was as conscious of hierarchies as any feudal court. As far as I could see, the democratic mixing of workman beside high official simply wasn't the Soviet way – whatever their propaganda might have you believe. If Gariachi was up there with the brass, I was pretty certain he was not just a sweeper of leaves and polisher of cars.

In the photographs, he was wearing a smart suit and there was a well-dressed middle-aged woman beside him who was, presumably, his wife. I had already marked him down as a tough-looking individual. He had a lean body and craggy face with deep-set eyes and without his workman's jacket, there was a definite military look about him.

I told Jay about the photographs at the next debriefing and we agreed that, properly analysed, they might teach us a lot about the real structure of the Soviet hierarchy in London, especially as there were a number of embassy people from Kensington at the banquet and it would be fascinating to see what common interests were reflected in the seating arrangements.

'Any chance of getting the photos out?' Jay asked.

'I don't see why not,' I said. 'The guards are bored out of their minds. I should be able to cash in on that.'

I noticed that Jay no longer went through the motions of telling me not to take unnecessary risks. I was pleased about that because it showed that he was coming to rely on my own judgement of what was possible and what wasn't and he quickly agreed when I asked him to find me a couple of group photographs similar to the ones on the board.

It wasn't in fact, a very difficult request. The table groupings were similar to a hundred office parties, or Rotary or official functions. The only problem was the uniforms but the photos looked as though they had been behind glass for some time and I doubted whether anyone would examine them very closely.

So, over the next three weeks, I removed the photographs, one by one. There were not many opportunities, which is why it took so long, but I kept the fake photographs in my briefcase and whenever I had a moment alone, I whipped open the glass case and substituted one of mine for one of theirs. During this period, I used to meet Mike most lunch-times and he had quick access to the van with photo-

64

graphic and copying equipment on board. On most days, the photograph was back in place by the afternoon – only once did I have to risk leaving a phoney one in overnight as there was simply no chance of being alone in the hall before we finished work.

Jay was delighted with the results and so, I gathered, were his superiors. The MI6 analysts were able to surmise a great deal about the links between Kensington and individuals in the Trade Delegation, as well as picking out at least one other person, in addition to Gariachi, who probably had a status superior to his apparent job.

Later, I became much more deeply involved with Gariachi, but the immediate importance of the photographs was that it encouraged Jay to get round to what had obviously been in his mind for some time: proposing that I should plant electronic listening devices inside the Trade Delegation.

If he had asked me outright to bug the Trade Delegation when he first offered me a chance at the double-glazing contract, I might well have had some misgivings. I would probably have accepted anyway, but Jay was careful to ease me into the job, convincing me initially that working against the Russians would be less dangerous than some of the work I had done previously for police intelligence.

Now, more than three months into the contract, there was no question of my refusing to place the bugs. I had confidence in Jay and I was just as keen as he was to get the most out of my incredible position inside the Trade Delegation.

Jay had prepared the ground nicely. He had gently massaged my ego by letting me know on several occasions how impressed his own superiors were with my work. I knew what he was going – but it was still a nice feeling.

I was pleased that I was working for MI6, the élite intelligence service; they were covering me and taking care of me and I was proving again and again that I could deliver what I had been hired to deliver. Making use of the photographs in the assembly hall had been my own idea and everyone had taken it as a sign that I was really hitting my stride.

I did have to admit though that electronic surveillance was

a completely new line for me. When Jay asked me directly if I had ever used bugging equipment, I had to confess that my experience was very limited. On two police undercover operations, I had worn a wire, but in both cases it had been a very straightforward device: a tiny microphone concealed under my shirt, linked to a miniature tape-recorder.

'We have some really sophisticated devices for you this time,' Jay said, 'but don't worry, we'll try and plant them for you.'

I asked what he meant and Jay said simply, 'You'll have a customer at the factory shortly, for a patio door. Make sure you supply the exact model you'll be fitting in the Trade Delegation assembly hall.'

Soon afterwards, we did receive a special order for a patio door. Two people I had never done business with before arrived at the factory, paid cash, and took the door away.

When I next saw Jay, he said, 'Our technical people are working with it. We're seeing if we can fit the listening devices into the grooves in the sliders. It'll take some time. In the meantime, you concentrate on cars.'

Cars were Jay's current obsession, though I was the one who had got him interested in the first place. During the early days in the assembly hall, when I couldn't find anything particularly useful to do, I had taken to paying attention to the comings and goings of the vehicles on the apron at the front of the complex which was easily visible from where we were working.

I did not expect a lot to come out of it, but I knew that Jay was interested in anything which made selective surveillance easier to organise. MI6 had a permanent manpower problem. They simply did not have the personnel to tail all the vehicles which might be worthwhile; anything I could do to pinpoint a car which was definitely being used by people who were a specific target, make a significant contribution to reducing Jay's surveillance budget.

Jay's interest had quickened even further when I noticed three vehicles with ordinary British licence plates which did not appear to belong to visitors. They were average mid-size saloon cars of various makes, but they had no markings at all

66

to indicate that they were diplomatic or Trade Delegation vehicles. I recorded the numbers and passed them on to Jay. Ten days later I received another round of congratulations.

'That was a really nice one, Bill,' Jay said. 'We've traced those cars back to a dealer in South London who's been laundering plates for the Russians.'

Unmarked, unrecorded vehicles are one of the best possible work tools for Soviet intelligence; they could go literally anywhere in the British Isles unnoticed. Unless the driver was careless and committed a traffic offence or became involved in an accident, the likelihood of their ever coming to the attention of the police was effectively nil. Acquiring a British-registered vehicle, though, was not all that straightforward. They had to find a sympathetic – or greedy – dealer who would turn a blind eye to any flaws in the documentation and not check closely on the particulars of the vehicle's keeper, since the real private addresses of Soviet personnel were all, in theory, known to the Home Office and to the Driver Vehicle Licensing Centre in Swansea. Jay's operatives had now discovered that all the illicit vehicles in the Trade Delegation had been supplied by the same man. He was never approached by the authorities. Jay got more mileage out of the find by keeping him under close surveillance and making sure that further vehicles which passed into Soviet hands were know to British security – and another little notch was added to our tally of successes.

In the meantime, however, Jay's technicians had not been as successful in their efforts to bug the patio doors. I had not yet seen the electronic equipment they were planning to use, but I was not surprised when Jay reported a short time later than there had not been enough room to conceal the bugs successfully in the slider grooves.

There were no prizes for guessing what was coming next!

'How do you feel about placing the bugs yourself?' Jay asked casually, when he had finished his account of the technician's failure.

'Whatever made me think you'd get around to asking that,' I said, with a grin. 'I must be psychic. Yes, hell, why not. In for a penny in for a pound.'

67

The next part of the briefing has to remain confidential even now as Jay reminded me very forcibly that the exact details of the equipment we were going to use were covered by the Official Secrets Act, particularly as it was a field in which the British are especially advanced.

I didn't care about the details of the bugs' performance. I was just reassured by their size and I felt confident that, given a reasonable amount of luck, I could plant them without too much trouble.

Jay gave me seven bugs in all. 'Place them at your own discretion,' he said, 'but try to get one near the lectern in the conference hall, if you can. We'd dearly like to hear at first hand what they have to say at their in-house meetings.'

I debated whether to take the bugs into the Trade Delegation immediately or whether to do a further recce and plan where they might go. I decided in favour of acting straightaway. I didn't really need any more reconnaissance; I could have drawn the layout of the concert hall and ajacent areas blind-folded and thinking about the problems and dangers of planting the bugs wasn't going to make me any more ready.

I took them in the very next day and I can truthfully say that I wasn't even really nervous. I had known for a long time that this day was coming and now that it had, I found I was able to feel quite detached as I weighed up the security situation.

Indeed, it looked exceptionally promising. Boredom had really set in with the guards by now and the scene that day was typical of the pattern that had developed. I had deliberately arrived late to give everyone time to settle down. Marat wasn't around and young Alexis was in charge of the escort detail – if you can be said to be in charge of anything with your head buried in a book. He was in one of the big chairs in the library, with his feet draped over the arm, totally absorbed in some paperback. I had three men on site that day and they were all working outside on the high ladders. I couldn't hear much banging and hammering which probably meant they were taking a little break, out of sight of Mr Denushenko. It doesn't take my lads long to get the hang of regulations and they had already developed their own routine for getting round the ban on alcohol on the premises.

They had begun by slipping a couple of cans of Long Life into their toolbags, but they had then figured out that some of the guards didn't object to drink themselves, or to making a pound or two by selling them vodka from the official store. Someone would pass the word to a friendly guard that a little trip to the shop would be appreciated and the lads would vanish up to the heights with some genuine Russian vodka to ward off the cold. I knew what was going on and turned a blind eye. I was not worried about safety; there isn't a building site in the world where a jar or two isn't consumed and my men were too concerned for their own skins to do anything silly on the ladders. Also it suited me perfectly. I was quite happy for them to have their breaks out of my sight, rather than keep coming down and brewing up in the leisure areas.

When I had taken in the security situation, I decided it was as good as it was going to be. I was not worried about concealed cameras. One of the big advantages of doing building work is that you have an excuse to examine the very skin of the building and I was quite satisfied that there were no hidden eyes anywhere in the assembly hall area. The only surveillance cameras I had come across in the entire complex, so far, were the ones installed for external security and directed outwards to monitor the areas around the entrances.

Amazingly, it took less than an hour to plant the bugs. I knew already where I wanted to put them. It was simply a matter of not moving too quickly and finding a proper reason for being in each particular place.

I took care of Jay's main concern by planting the first one on the lectern, a pulpit-like structure which dominated the conference hall. It was an old-fashioned, almost Victorian design, with deep grooves and ornamentation where the reading shelf joined the pedestal and the tiny gadget slipped in easily. I put the second one at the side of the stage and a third behind the laths on the wall near the screen which was used for slides and film shows. One of the easiest to place was under the billiard table – the only problem was whether it would get clogged with dust as no one seemed to have cleaned the under-surface for years.

The library was more difficult because that was cleaned regularly. There were not many nooks and corners in the structure of the walls themselves and the books were dusted almost every other day. I had made a point of watching the cleaners at work and although two or three different women did the job, the routine did not vary much.

The cleaner always wiped the front of the shelves and dusted most of the rows of books, but no one ever bothered to get the special ladder and go right up to the top shelf. I used my own ladder and on the pretext of inspecting a window fitting, I slipped a bug in behind the L-shaped support holding the highest shelf. I put the sixth bug in the children's room, not because I expected Jay to get much out of spying on kids, but because it was an annexe which was often borrowed for adult meetings. That was six. One left to go. There was no obvious place left, but I had an idea which later turned out to have been a touch of inspiration: I put the last one in the men's loo!

I intended to place the bug behind the cistern but it was an old-fashioned Shanks model so the tank was too high up. Instead, I slipped it behind a small section under the pan, well out of reach of even the most diligent of cleaners, to judge from the accumulation of dirt there.

When all seven were in place, I could hardly believe that it had gone so smoothly. I reported to Jay that same evening and could see he was delighted. He held back his congratulations though until he had quizzed me in the minutest detail about where I had placed each one. Together we went over everything I knew about the routines of the Trade Delegation to be sure I hadn't overlooked some activity which would make it likely the bugs would be found.

When he was satisfied, he gave me a huge grin and produced a bottle of single malt. 'To the beginning of a new era,' he said. 'I'll get the wagons out tomorrow.'

The 'wagons' were the MI6 surveillance vans which were stationed around Hampstead Heath in various guises for many months to come.

Everyone was ecstatic, but one of the tantalising things about the bugging operation was that my own direct role in it was so brief. I was very proud of the fact that I had brought it off, yet in terms of time my contribution was really very short. Jay never gave me many details of what his monitors learned but he left me in no doubt, over and over again, that I had made possible a coup beyond everyone's expectations. Jay's only complaint ever, in fact, was that he could never get his hands on enough interpreters and translators! I did learn though from the general tone of Jay's comments that the information collected from the bugs had opened up a whole new range of investigations for MI6, identifying new people to be watched, and also the latest targets that the Russians were trying to achieve in their espionage activities. The bugs also highlighted the role being played by the Trade Delegation. Jay confided once that MI6 had had the impression that Soviet Intelligence had become concentrated in the embassy in Kensington, but the material collected by the 'wagons' left no one in any doubt that the Delegation was more than doing its share.

I would like to have asked many more questions than I did, but I knew that Jay would not pass the information on to me. It was not in my interest any more than it was in his. The less I knew, the less chance there was that I might give something away in conversation with a member of the Trade Delegation; it was better, Jay felt, to keep my reactions to individuals genuine – until I discovered for myself something which established that they were engaged in activities other than those for which they were officially designated. The real reason for Jay's secrecy though was that I did not need to know what was being found out. I just needed to see that my work was worthwhile, and Jay left me in no doubt about that.

However, I was very curious about the technical effectiveness of the surveillance. I could scarcely believe that a 'wagon' or van situated a mile away on Hampstead Heath could monitor such wide areas clearly, using such tiny bugs. Jay would not let me into the vans – the equipment was too secret even for me to lay eyes on – but he did arrange a little test for me.

When I questioned him about the range of the bugs and the quality of the transmission, he said, 'All right, Bill, it's only fair you should know how good they are. Here's what you do. When you're in the building tomorrow, give us a little tune. Just hum, or whistle, or sing something while you're working. It doesn't have to be too loud.' He grinned. 'Better pick something appropriate. Why not "The Red Flag"?'

The next day, I did just that. I went round the assembly hall and library, singing almost under my breath a few verses of 'The Red Flag'. I made the test as hard as possible because in the back of my mind, I still didn't really believe Jay.

Later at the 'shop', Jay produced a tape and say, 'Well, Bill, we've made you into a pop star.'

When I heard the recording, I just could not believe it. The quality was absolutely stunning. You could hear every note and at one point, when I coughed, it came through as though we were in the same room.

'Trust me Bill,' Jay said. 'The translators are working overtime. And by the way, we're getting fantastic results from the one in the toilet. That's where they do most of their grumbling!'

After that my role in the bugging operation was limited to keeping an eye open for any changes in Trade Delegation routines which might make it more likely the bugs would be found – and having periodic discussions with Jay about how much longer we dare leave them in.

It took us more than six months to finish all the work in the assembly hall and adjoining areas, but I managed to convince Jay that there was no need to take the bugs out even then.

The scale of the work was such that I had plenty of reasons for going back afterwards to make sure individual pieces of equipment were working properly. I just said I wanted to check this slider, or that joint and no special security precautions were taken because I had been in the Trade Delegation for months without apparently arousing any suspicion.

We prolonged the bugging operations until finally Jay said, reluctantly, that it would have to come to an end.

'We can't keep going indefinitely, Bill, much as I'd love to,' he said. 'They've been in the best part of nine months. Let's not push our luck.'

Perhaps the most amazing thing about the whole bugging operation – at least from my point of view – was the speed with which it ended.

The decision was taken and I got the bugs out in ten minutes! One morning, I made an excuse to go back into the assembly hall, carried out an inspection tour of the various points I wanted to examine, and pocketed the bugs one after the other.

Throughout the operation, Jay deliberately kept most the details from me, but when it was over, he summed it up with real feeling:

'By God Bill,' he said. 'We've struck at them and we've struck at them hard.'

CHAPTER 7

I enjoyed the next stage of the operation even more than the bugging because my role in it was more personal. Jay wanted me to trap and subvert a member of the Trade Delegation staff: the man who almost chose himself as victim was the mysterious Mr Gariachi.

We had been interested in Gariachi ever since I had noticed on the banquet photograph his elevation from sweeper of leaves and polisher of cars to a seat on the top table at the Trade Delegation's biggest annual function. For two or three months I had no real chance to get close to him, but gradually he began to take more and more turns as one of the escort detail and he became a member of what I called the 'boiler-house group'.

The boiler house had become the unofficial social centre and skiving-off place for myself and my men. We were almost into our second winter in the Trade Delegation and a warm, cosy spot for unofficial breaks was sorely needed. I had found the boiler house quite early on in the contract when I had been looking for a place to store windows and other materials. It was a large room at the back of the main building, much like any other boiler house except that it was spotlessly clean and there was a lot of extra space in it, in addition to the area which housed the actual boilers.

Part of it, for example, was used for milk deliveries. There were pigeon holes for each flat and room and the milkman who called daily left the appropriate number of pints in each. I liked it because it was well out of the way; people rarely dropped in unexpectedly and it was not in the area covered by the surveillance cameras which recorded the comings and goings through the gates of the complex.

When Gariachi started to take on spells of escort duty, he also took an immediate liking to the boiler house. He seemed to enjoy the warmth and, like the other guards, he was quite ready to use it for a few minutes and often for a lot longer – for a break from the boredom of watching us work.

I was intrigued by Gariachi from the outset. Superficially, he seemed a nice enough chap; he had a friendly manner and his attitude to life seemed to be that he wanted to enjoy himself as much as he could in this particular posting, but I sensed that he was missing Moscow and home.

Despite his casual manner though, he was definitely a hard man. He was physically strong and his rugged features and hard-bitten face left you in no doubt that he could handle himself in a tight corner.

He contrasted very strongly with the other man who joined the boiler house group about that time, a younger man whom we knew as Valerya. He was small and thin and slightly effeminate. He gave the impression at first that he might be gay, but when I got to know him better, I decided that he wasn't. I found Valerya a bit off-putting because he had a way of suddenly appearing at your side and standing very close. One second he was nowhere to be seen; the next he was standing practically toe-to-toe. Most of the Russians we dealt with had a very positive, military step, but Valerya used to creep about almost stealthily. I liked him better when I got to know him but you always had to be careful because he was one of the most inquisitive men I came across; he was always asking questions so that you had to be constantly on your guard so as not to let anything slip.

On the whole, I preferred Gariachi's company and he seemed to be at ease with me, especially as I was able to cement our friendship a little by doing him a favour. When the work on the concert hall and library was finished, the contract was renewed for a third stage, to double-glaze a series of flats, known as Millfield Flats because they faced onto Millfield Road which made up one of the largest sections of the complex.

Gariachi told me that his was one of the flats scheduled for double-glazing and asked if I could do it first. When I checked with the list of orders for materials I found that his windows had already arrived and I made a big play of

75

agreeing, as a favour, even though it didn't actually make any difference to the schedule.

I did not learn much more about him from the flat because I was alone for hardly any of the time the work was being done. But we became quite friendly and then, by accident, alcohol came to my aid, to carry things a step further.

I had met Mike for a drink at lunch-time and decided to make an exception to my normal cautious rules by taking a couple of cans of Long Life back in the pocket of my duffle coat. When I got back I found Gariachi alone in the boiler house, reading a copy of *Time* magazine. I offered him a beer and he drank it with such gusto that it barely touched the sides of his throat. I didn't want to let enthusiasm like that go to waste so I said, 'Look, it's nice and warm in here and I'm not really in a working mood. How would it be if I sent one of my chaps down in the van for a few more cans?'

Gariachi was more than ready, so I asked Kevin Daley to go down to the off-licence and we soon had a nice little session going. It didn't do a lot of good for the double-glazing contract but it certainly paid off with Gariachi and did no harm to morale generally, especially as it was a bitterly cold day.

Up to that point, Gariachi had been pleasant enough, but once he was drinking he really began to warm up. My men were coming and going, popping in from time to time for a quick one, then going back up the ladders with Gariachi chatting freely to all of them. I sensed just how relaxed he was when we started talking about Ivan Koften, the man my chaps always referred to as Mighty Mouse, because he was built like a miniature wrestler.

I said casually, 'I hope Mr Koften doesn't catch us like this. I don't suppose he'd be too pleased.'

I wanted to see how Gariachi would respond and his answer was beyond anything I had expected.

'You don't like Mr Koften?' he said.

'I don't mind him,' I said cautiously, 'but I don't think he's what you'd call one of the boys. In fact, between you and me, some of the guards have told us he's a bit of a bastard.'

'He is second in command to Mr Denushenko,' Gariachi

said, 'and when he gets back to Moscow, he will get promotion.' He paused. 'That is what he is working for. Tell your chaps to be careful in their conversations. He reports everything to Mr Denushenko. What you say – and what we say too.'

'Really?' I said.

'Koften is not like me,' Gariachi said. 'I have been doing this job a long time. He is much younger. He is very ambitious. And do not think that because he does not say much, he does not speak English. He understands it perfectly.'

It was the first time I had heard anyone speak so frankly about the internal politics of the Trade Delegation, and I was surprised too that it should be Gariachi; it is amazing what effect a few cans of beer can have, but I certainly wasn't complaining.

I gave him another beer and he kept the conversation rolling nicely. He told me that he had been in Cuba and several South American countries and he admitted that, though he liked England, he would be glad to get home. I asked him what his main job in the building was and he came straight out and said, 'Security'. He explained that one of his regular tasks was to make sure that all the doors in the Trade Delegation were locked at night and opened in the morning.

I played a bit naive and asked if that was a full-time job. He took the question seriously and explained that the Soviet Union was very security conscious and his work was regarded as extremely important. At the same time, he virtually admitted that one of his tasks was to do internal reports on individuals in the Trade Delegation.

'We are not as lackadaisical as you people, Bill,' he said. 'The way your people work, with these long breaks. It would not be allowed in the Soviet Union.'

I said, 'Oh a break now and then does no harm. It just makes my men work harder. My chaps find some of your ways a bit strange, but everyone seems to get on all right. In fact,' I said, 'as you have been so nice to us, I would very much to treat you and Valerya to a night out. Do you fancy coming out for an evening at the pub?'

77

I knew I was taking a bit of a chance by appearing eager, but Gariachi jumped at the idea.

'That's great,' I said, 'how about Tuesday? Do you know a pub called The Duke of St Albans?'

'Tuesday is fine,' Gariachi said, 'but The Duke of St Albans is a bit near the Trade Delegation. Could we go a bit further away?'

I got the point and we agreed on The Bull and Last, and I walked out of the boiler house that afternoon with the distinct feeling that I had made a breakthrough.

I reported it to Jay the same evening and he too was delighted. I was – to put it mildly – in a pretty cheerful mood by then, after the lunch-time session with Mike and an afternoon drinking with Gariachi, and I was very glad that we had a new system now for getting to the de-briefings which did not involve me in too much walking.

Once we had started bugging the Trade Delegation, Jay had insisted on extra security precautions to make sure we had an early warning if the Russians started to become suspicious by taking a special interest in me. 'Leave it to me,' Jay had said. 'We'll pick you up and make you vanish into thin air.'

From that time on, the system of meeting Mike in a pub and going on with him to the 'shop' was abandoned. After work I would go straight home from the Trade Delegation in the company van and have my tea. After tea, I would go out, ostensibly for a stroll, and make for a narrow alley some way from the house which was blocked at both ends by bollards to prevent cars from using it.

That particular alley had been chosen because it was easy to watch me as I approached it from the end nearest the house and so be sure I wasn't being followed.

At the other end, an MI6 car would wait, out of sight, to pick me up. Seconds later, we were away, heading in one of a dozen different directions before anyone could run through the alleyway after me and see where I had gone. If anyone had been seen to follow me – though it never actually happened – the MI6 car would have been warned by radio and would have moved away before I reached the end of the alley. The drill was that if I found the car wasn't there, I would continue my stroll into Alexander Palace, have a pint at my local, and come home again, having done nothing to arouse suspicion.

The system suited me very well because it meant that I had far less walking and riding on tubes to do. In fact, I had transport all the way from the Trade Delegation to the de-briefing, with a 'pit stop' at home to have something to eat.

I asked Jay that night if he had any specific instructions for handling the pub meeting with Gariachi and Valerya, but he said he was happy to let me play the situation as it came.

'You're doing fine, Bill,' he said. 'Just carry on the way you are. But make sure you leave the pub with them. We'll keep an eye on you.'

That meant there would be a camera team in place, but I didn't ask for details as I had learned from experience that the less you know, the less self-conscious you are about the idea of having your movements recorded.

The next evening, I got to The Bull and Last just after the time we had agreed and found Gariachi already at the bar, but there was no sign of Valerya. 'I'm sorry, Bill,' Gariachi said, 'he couldn't get away. A special party was arranged at the Delegation. It was sprung on us at the last minute. Some visitors from Scotland.'

I probed a bit and gathered that they were representatives of a Scottish company which was doing business with the Trade Delegation. I got the name, without seeming too inquisitive, but I didn't want to spoil our first meeting on neutral ground by putting him on his guard so I decided to let the matter drop and leave Jay to follow up on the Scots.

At one point, Gariachi said, 'You're not Scottish are you, Bill?' I presumed he was giving me a little test as I was sure he must have remembered our conversations about Ireland, so I reminded him gently and he said, 'Oh that's right. Most of you chaps seem to be Irish.'

'Yes,' I said, 'almost all of us. We're an Irish company really.' Gariachi didn't ask whether I was Northern Irish but that did not surprise me. No one in the Trade Delegation seemed to make a distinction between the North and the South and the question would not have bothered me anyway as most of my chaps were from the Republic.

We talked a bit about the men and Gariachi had obviously been observing their habits quite closely. 'Kevin is funny, isn't he?' Gariachi said. 'He likes jokes.' He smiled. 'And he likes Russian sweets too.'

Inevitably the conversation soon turned to football. I told him how I had watched Moscow Dynamo play against Arsenal when I was a kid and had always remembered it. He said his own team was Kiev but he liked watching Chelsea and had already been to Stamford Bridge. I joked with him that he ought to come and see Arsenal and watch a decent team play, and the evening went on from there, very much in the vein of normal pub chat.

Eventually, I managed to turn the talk round to his family. I had gathered already from double-glazing his flat that he had family with him in London, but I pretended that I hadn't noticed particularly and let him tell me about his wife and two children. I asked if he had any photos of them and he said not with him but he promised to show me some other time. He did not suggest a meeting though and I guessed that he wanted to keep his pub evenings as a night out with the boys.

All in all, it was a good start to our relationship outside the Trade Delegation and I would have been quite content if that had been all that happened, but before the end of the evening, I had a spectacular stroke of luck: Gariachi ran out of money.

I had deliberately been drinking quite fast, in an attempt to loosen him up again. He had stayed level however, choosing lager and apparently really enjoying it. I had tried to make the evening my treat but he had insisted on paying for alternate rounds, then, at one point well on into the evening, when it was my turn to buy, Gariachi hesitated.

'I'd like another one, Bill,' he said, 'but financially, I am not in a position to buy you one back.'

'Oh, don't worry about that,' I said, trying not to let my excitment show. 'Do you need some money?'

I reached instantly into my wallet and offered him £20. Gariachi looked at it for a moment then he took £10 and made a sign to me to keep the rest.

'We are paid on Thursdays,' he said. 'I will give it back then. Is that all right?'

'Don't worry about paying me back,' I said. 'Just get me some of those nice big bottles of vodka from the Trade Delegation shop.'

Gariachi's face lit up. 'You prefer that?'

'Yes,' I said. 'Much.'

'That is fine,' Gariachi said. 'I will have the vodka for you tomorrow.'

After that, he relaxed completely and I made a point of not turning the conversation to anything which might bother him. I had made a pal, and that was what I wanted most at that stage.

Not surprisingly, Jay was also very satisfied with the situation. He was already enthusiastic about the meeting on neutral ground and he greeted me cheerfully, with a beautiful glossy print of Gariachi and me leaving The Bull and Last, but when I told him about the money, I really had his attention.

'I don't have to tell you what an opening you've got there, Bill,' he said. I thought for a moment that Jay was going to ask me to make a direct approach to Gariachi and try to entice him with money at which point I would start to dig in my heels. I felt I was getting far too much valuable information to risk everything by stepping out of character, but I need not have worried – Jay had something quite different in mind.

'Oh Christ no,' Jay said. 'We don't want you to do anything like that. This is one for our dirty tricks brigade. We'll give Mr Gariachi a nice little shock. You just remember two things: whenever you meet him for a drink, try to make sure it's always in The Bull and Last and if any more money does change hands, make sure it's done in full view; don't let him take it under the table.'

I went ahead exactly as Jay instructed, but I knew I had to be careful with Gariachi. On the face of it, he was enjoying our new friendship as much as I was. He seemed to have had a good time at The Bull and Last; the bottles of vodka were delivered promptly, and at our next meeting in the boiler house, a couple of days later, he was all ready to get straight at

81

the cans of beer. Nevertheless, I never relaxed for a moment. If I had been asked to pick out one Russian in the Trade Delegation who most resembled myself, I would have chosen Gariachi. I could not shake off the feeling that he might be just as alert as I was – and playing the same kind of game.

As long as I stayed on my guard, I wasn't worried. I wasn't actually doing anything wrong, at least not anything that wasn't in my character as a free-drinking amiable Irish workman. I wasn't asking the wrong questions, or trying to bribe him; I was merely offering him a loan and accepting repayment in black market vodka, something most of my chaps would do – in fact were already doing – with the other guards.

As far as I could judge, Gariachi was glad of a chance to relax. He seemed to be under a certain amount of strain, possibly because of his long spells in Cuba and South America before coming to England, but that could have been an act too, and I always allowed for that possibility.

I went ahead exactly as though our relationship were genuine, and we certainly did seem to be hitting it off. If anything, Gariachi seemed to enjoy the boiler house sessions almost more than the pub. Perhaps he felt more secure there; certainly it was nicely off all the usual routes through the complex, and was a genuinely cosy place for a drink and a chat.

At our next boiler house session, after a couple of cans of beer, Gariachi proudly produced some photographs of his family and in one of them, he was in Russian army uniform.

I examined it very closely, complimented him on his wife and made a joke about how much smarter he looked then than he did now. I could see from the uniform that he was not an officer, but although I did not know enough about Russian military insignia to be sure of his exact rank, it was obvious that, even at the time of the photograph when he was several years younger, he was well above ordinary private soldier.

I noted carefully the details of the uniform but I deliberately did not ask any pointed questions. He said, without prompting, that he had been in tanks in those days and had trained as a radar specialist.

I asked, innocently, if he was still liable to be called back for service, or whether his reserve commitment was over.

'As a matter of fact, Bill,' he said. 'I am a long-term soldier. I am still in the army!'

I finally had the clincher. We had been right. Gariachi was not just an ex-soldier engaged as a security guard; the evidence of the banquet photograph had turned out to be correct. Within a week, Jay had obtained Gariachi's details. Knowing that he was still a serving soldier and knowing roughly the dates of his previous postings, Jay established that he was now a warrant officer, the approximate equivalent of a company sergeant major, – a substantial rank in the Soviet security service and well above the status recorded on his application for diplomatic entry through the Home Office.

The idea that we had on our hands a security man of that kind of standing who was willing to borrow money from a casual British acquaintance really tantalised Jay and I was told to do everything I could to work Gariachi round to the idea of coming back for another loan, without of course being too blatant about it and scaring him off.

There was now added urgency because Gariachi told me during one of our boiler house sessions that a new team of guards was coming in to take over escort duties. He slipped me the information as a friend and agreed, with a wink, that he would put in a good word for me when they briefed the incoming crew.

Given enough time, I was sure Gariachi would run short of money again and turn to me, but if he was assigned to other duties, the pub sessions might well draw to a close before they had properly begun.

I took the chance and suggested another evening at The Bull and Last earlier than I would have liked to. Gariachi agreed without hesitation and this time, he brought Valerya.

I was ready, with wallet bulging, and so, it seemed, was Jay, as I noticed straightaway that the pub had a new landlord. The regular publican was a fair-haired chap with a rather pretty wife – I had come to know the couple quite well. Now there was a stocky red-haired man who told me, when I asked in normal bar room chat, that he was standing in for three weeks while the landlord helped out in a pub that was having trouble.

The evening with Gariachi and Valerya turned out to be very enjoyable – but it was also really tantalising. Several times, I thought Gariachi was gearing himself up to ask me for money, but each time the conversation took another tack, right at the last minute.

Everyone was in a relaxed mood and I started off by saying that I was considering making a trip to Moscow. I said that if the contract at the Trade Delegation was finished in time, I thought I would try and see the Olympic Games and I asked, jokingly, what the girls were like in Moscow, and whether Gariachi would show me a good time.

Both he and Valerya seemed keen on the idea and they obviously took it as an indication that I was enjoying my work for the Russians. Gariachi said that, as a foreign visitor, I would be obliged to stay at the special tourist hotels, but he would certainly meet me and take me round if he was back home by then.

From there, the conversation drifted inevitably into sport and, of course, into football. I noticed that they were both very relaxed in the English pub setting. They had no trouble ordering and they could lean on the bar and down their pints of lager like old hands, and do a spot of girl-watching, though they never gave any indication that they would consider approaching one.

The only thing they weren't fully at ease with was the juke box. They both liked music, but I was the one who had to pick the records and operate the machine. I am not very well up on the charts myself, but they really only liked ballads and their big favourite was Cliff Richard, so I usually chose one of his numbers and threw in the odd Irish song for variety.

When they had had a few lagers, they started joking about the black market that was developing with my men, and though I was happy to have the conversation turning round to money, I was a bit uneasy when they told me just how deeply some of the chaps were getting involved. From the way Gariachi was talking, it seemed a wonder that Kevin Daley had any room in his toolbag for his tools; I gathered they had established regular prices and supply dates for cigarettes and vodka, and were now beginning to branch out into other things, including the beautiful suede jackets that were a speciality of the official shop.

I said I wasn't too happy about the situation because I didn't want Denushenko finding out and cancelling my contract because of the backstairs dealing. Gariachi laughed. 'Don't worry, Bill,' he said. 'It is the guards who do the selling and we are in charge of security . . . '

I couldn't help laughing. Things really are the same the world over.

But there was still no suggestion of another loan. I decided finally that it must be because Valerya was there; during the conversation about black market dealings, I was sure Gariachi would have like to touch me for a few pounds, but he held back and there was nothing I could do about it.

The moment came, finally, more than a week later, when we had a third evening in The Bull and Last and when, again, Valerya was tied up at the Trade Delegation.

'It is difficult for us to get out together, Bill,' Gariachi said apologetically. 'Usually we have to work one on, one off.'

I sensed straightaway that the moment for the touch was coming and it did – before we were halfway through the evening. Gariachi didn't seem at all embarrassed this time. Presumably he had decided that I was glad to be in on the black market too and he said, almost casually, 'By the way, Bill, do you have any spare cash tonight?'

'Sure,' I said, 'how much would you like?'

Gariachi grinned. 'Is twenty pounds all right?'

My God you learn fast, I thought, as I reached into my wallet. 'No problem,' I said, 'just keep the vodka coming.'

I handed him four five pound notes, making sure they were spread out and clearly visible with neither my fingers nor Gariachi's obscuring the handover. Gariachi did not seem at all concerned. He made no attempt to hide the money, taking it matter-of-factly, as though I were repaying a loan to him – and it made a lovely piece of cinema.

I had thought Jay would be taking only still pictures, but a week later he showed me the whole transaction on film. Every detail was perfect. Gariachi's face and mine were as sharp as you could want and the handing over of the money was as clear as if a director had arranged the moves.

'We've got him,' Jay said triumphantly. 'Soviet security officials just don't take money from foreigners in pubs. When we approach him, he'll either play ball or go to the wall.'

Jay grinned at me. 'Don't worry. There'll be no come-back on you. Mr Gariachi won't find out about the film until he's back in Moscow. He can be more use to us there than here. Bill, you did a fantastic job.'

There was a steely look in Jay's eyes which reminded me more forcibly than his words that he was very much a field-man, not a desk-bound bureaucrat. There was a ruthlessness in the way he talked about using Gariachi that left no doubt that he knew how the intelligence game is played in the real world.

One of the hardest tasks for our intelligence people in Moscow is to develop contacts within Soviet intelligence and the military. This kind of hold over a man like Gariachi could be used to force him to gather information for us, or to collaborate in helping us to trace someone – a dissident or someone in detention on whom we wanted to keep tabs. Gariachi would be in no doubt that his career would be over instantly if the photos were ever shown to the Soviet authorities. Even if they believed his explanation, he would be guilty of gross carelessness for a professional; if they did not believe his explanation, he could be at much greater risk. Gariachi was a man who knew a great deal about the nuts and bolts of Soviet security, both in Moscow and abroad, in other centres like Cuba where he had served. MI6 would have a choice of ways in which they could use him.

I liked Gariachi a lot, but I had no regrets about trapping him. He was no innocent victim. He had a background and training in security just like I had. It had been a contest between equals and he had made the wrong move and lost. Now, it was up to Jay's people to decide the price of his failure.

CHAPTER 8

I had quite a few surprises during my time inside the Soviet Trade Delegation but one of the biggest was when I first set eyes on a man we nicknamed the 'Biker'. Really, it wasn't so much a nickname as an accurate description, as he could well have been on his way to a meeting of the local chapter of the Hell's Angels.

I saw him first at about eleven o'clock one morning on the main staircase of the section of the complex known as Millfield Flats where we were engaged on the third stage of our double-glazing contract. And what a sight he looked! He was about twenty-two or twenty-three, with long, straggly, greasy hair and a biker's jacket covered with so many badges that you could hardly see the leather. He had oil-stained trousers tucked into motorcycle boots and looked generally so scruffy that I was amazed he was allowed out of his room. The standard of dress at the Trade Delegation was always extremely conservative. The men mostly wore dark suits or jackets and the women generally had on rather sober dresses or skirts and blouses. Some of the wives of the senior staff were very smart, but their style always tended to be severe. The only splashes of colour you saw were among the schoolchildren, and even then it was usually an ordinary blue or orange anorak worn over grey trousers or a plain school skirt. I would have expected Denushenko to take one look at this biker and march him off before his feet touched the ground.

For all his sleazy appearance though, this young man had a purposeful look about him. I waited by a window and watched him leave the complex by the side entrance and stride off over Hampstead Heath, and I could tell by the confident way he handled himself at the security check that this was not just the Delegation's black sheep drop-out.

I told Jay about him and he said, 'You're going to wreck my budget altogether if you go on like this. I've already got people following your Jewish couple and your Czechs. You're going to have to slow down.'

I laughed, knowing full well he did not mean it. Mike had told me several times that Jay was delighted with the information I was providing and that his budget was growing steadily, in proportion to the list of successes.

This latest stage in the Millfield Flats was producing a whole crop of new leads, though most of them had to be followed up by Jay's people outside the Trade Delegation. I was there to provide the essential starting point.

The Jewish couple Jay referred to had caught my attention because they were the oldest people I had seen in the Delegation. I had been surprised to find Jews at all in the building, but their features were so obviously semitic that there wasn't really any doubt, and their style of dress also had a Jewish look about it.

I came across them when we were about to begin a new flat. I went ahead to prepare for the fitters and found the couple dressed as though they were about to go out. The man was exceptionally smart, in an expensive-looking full length suede coat and the woman had a cloth coat with a big fur collar and stylish brooch.

I thought at first they were someone's parents visiting from Moscow, but the man began to give me instructions about doing the glazing which made me realise that the flat was definitely theirs. I watched them leave the Delegation by the side door and Jay decided that they were also worth a second look by the foot patrols.

The Czechs were another group I had set Jay on to, after a chance encounter. I had seen them first one evening when we happened to be leaving the Delegation much later than usual. The Russians had invited me and my men to a little party – drinks and sandwiches and a game of billiards and darts. We had left the van parked at the back of the building but I had decided to finish the evening down in Kentish Town and had walked out alone through the front entrance.

At the gate, I noticed Denushenko talking to a stylishly

dressed man and woman in a big white Mercedes limousine. I did not attach any special importance to them at the time, but Jay was always interested in visitors to the Delegation so I noted the number of the car and described the couple to him at the next debriefing. Jay told me straightaway from the number plate that it was a Czech embassy car and he commented that it was unusual for other Eastern bloc countries to have such open contacts with the Russians in London, despite their close political ties.

At a later session at the 'shop', he brought some photographs of Czech embassy staff. I picked the couple out without any hesitation and Jay said, 'Ah yes. We know quite a bit about them. I wonder what they were discussing with Denushenko.' He didn't elaborate but asked me to keep a sharp eye open in case they paid any further visits to the Trade Delegation.

As I write about these de-briefings now, it sounds very straightforward to say, 'Jay asked me to do this' or 'I reported that,' but it would be wrong to give the impression that we just met in the safe flat for a casual chat over a drink.

The de-briefings were exhausting. There is no other word for it. Over the months, Jay developed a technique which virtually doubled my work, ensuring that not even the tiniest detail was missed. I would arrive at the 'shop' and exchange a few pleasantries, then Jay would turn on the tape recorder and I would go through the day's events. I have been trained in observation and I know how important it is to go through each stage methodically. You can't skip anything. I had to relive the day almost minute by minute, listing all the people I had seen and giving the precise circumstances. I would pick faces out of the album of photographs or if they were not there, I would give detailed descriptions, including comments about people's moods and attitudes.

I had to describe the rooms in fine detail, too: how they were decorated and furnished; how they differed from other rooms; what objects had I seen which struck me as unusual or interesting. On top of that I supplied the numbers of every vehicle I had seen inside the Delegation on that day, with times of arrivals and departures if possible.

Jay would leave me to talk, then prod gently if he thought I might be leaving out some small point and only when he thought he had milked me dry would he turn off the tape recorder.

Still that was not the end of it. Far from it. When the de-briefing was technically over, Jay would break it off, bring out the drinks and as we sat, relaxing, he would turn the tape recorder on again and make me go over the same ground to see if I could add anything with my memory jogged by the drink.

Really, it was like being interrogated night after night. Though I was among friends and colleagues, the strain was similar to being subjected to formal questioning over and over again.

One of Jay's special skills was to recognise when I was flagging and find ways of building up my confidence and maintaining my enthusiasm. There is no doubt he 'played me' skilfully, keeping me struggling on, even when I felt absolutely whacked. His tried and tested way was to feed me with intriguing bits of information about the results that were coming out of my work. He would tell me nothing for days on end, then suddenly, when he sensed that I needed brisking up, he would say, 'Oh by the way, Bill, we've had a really interesting report back on your Czechs.'

They weren't actually my Czechs at all in this case, but Jay knew I was always fascinated to hear the backgrounds on the people I had been involved with.

One evening, he gave me the whole picture they had built up around the couple I had seen in the white Mercedes. They were what Jay called talent spotters, in other words, their mission in London was to spot people who might be recruitable by Czech intelligence. Their favourite technique was to offer a friendly shoulder to young people who were finding life in London lonely or depressing. Young Communist Party functions were one of their particular hunting grounds. Many young people drifted into left-wing politics because of a feeling of alienation from British society which was often brought on by personal problems, money troubles or lack of friends.

The Czech couple used to 'help out' in various hostels, not just those which housed students, but the ones which provided low-cost accommodation to young people just starting out in careers like the civil service. Other Czechs kept a watch on the exile community; this pair concentrated on English people and, under the guise of amateur social work, offered financial help if someone was struggling to keep ahead of the bills on a low salary.

That kind of evening, when Jay would outline the plan against the people I was helping to trap, gave me renewed energy because I felt part of the bigger operation and not just someone who noted car numbers and stole documents.

Nevertheless, by the time we had been on the contract for a year, I found the work was taking a serious toll, both mentally and physically.

In the first place, the days were so long. I would report to the Trade Delegation at eight o'clock and finish around five-thirty, and during those hours there was not a single moment of relaxation. My so-called breaks – the drinking sessions in the boiler house or my chats with Gariachi or Marat – far from being time off were often when I had to concentrate the hardest. I was always thinking on my feet, and looking ahead at the same time. When I woke up in the morning my mind would go straight into gear; I would start thinking 'How shall I set about getting that letter I spotted yesterday?' or 'How shall I handle Gariachi? He seemed a bit worried about this or that'. Nothing was simple; I was always planning three or four moves ahead.

Then came the de-briefing sessions which often continued late into the evening. I found that I was beginning to lose weight and my digestion was suffering too because, on most days, I was drinking too much and eating too little. My usual habit is to have a light breakfast before going to work, with snacks on site during the afternoon, then I have my main cooked meal at home in the evening. As the pace of the undercover work quickened, I was missing my main meal more and more often and I wasn't bothering to eat properly when I did finally get home as I had spoiled my appetite with a sandwich at the debriefing. Drinking had become a constant part of the work. The Russians liked me to drink with them, most of my meetings with Mike took place in pubs, and Jay liked me to have a jar or two at the de-briefings to ease my tensions so that he could drain out the last drop of information.

Through it all, one of Mike's special tasks, as he has subsequently admitted, was to monitor my mental state. If I seemed to be getting overtired or disgruntled, he would put in a report and Jay would find some way of boosting my morale to get me going again.

His reports on the Jewish couple were a classic example. He knew I was really intrigued by them because they were so far off the regular pattern of Trade Delegation life. Their elegance and general style, not to mention their age, set them apart and I kept asking Jay what they were up to.

Usually Jay answered, 'Oh, we're still looking into that,' deliberately stringing me along and saving up information until he felt I needed a boost.

One night, when I was really down, he said, 'Bill, did you know your Jewish couple are good at skittles and dominoes?'

'What?' I asked.

'That's right,' Jay said, 'and they play a lot of cards too. It's all part of their social life in Golders Green. They're real pillars of the older community up there. No one knows they have any connection with the Trade Delegation. They're supposed to have left the Soviet Union donkey's years ago. They spend their evenings in all the pubs and social clubs, mixing with their own generation. They know everyone, especially the people who have contacts or family inside the Soviet Union. They're always very sympathetic when some-one has a relative who wants to emigrate and can't get a visa. Always friendly, and ready with advice.' Jay grinned. 'But don't worry, we're putting a stop to their little game. We have friends in that community too, and the word has gone out. They're going to find their information is starting to dry up – and not before time. That harmless-looking old couple has done a hell of a lot of damage.'

I was really pleased because they had definitely been one of mine. Jay was already onto the Czechs, but if I hadn't spotted the Jewish couple, Jay's people would probably never have come across them, so I felt entitled to add them to my personal tally.

As Jay well knew, it was information like that which kept me going, but still there were weeks when I only just made it through to the weekend.

One of my favourite ways of spending Saturday is to get up late, have a lunch-time pint in the local, then come home and settle down in front of the television to watch the Saturday sport, and make a few bets on the horses to keep up the interest. After a year at the Trade Delegation, I was finding I was having trouble staying awake for the three pm start! Many's the time I settled down, looking forward to the afternoon's sport, fell asleep on the settee and woke up, feeling half-drugged in the middle of Saturday evening.

The biggest cause of the tiredness was tension. It was not fear; on this kind of assignment, I don't find that I feel afraid, mainly because I have learned that I can trust my instincts to give me advance warning if a hostile situation is building up. I think it comes mainly from my time as a prison officer. I can detect changes in people's attitudes very quickly. I can tell instantly, for example, if I am getting a reaction from someone like Denushenko or Gariachi that differs even a fraction from the normal, and I trust that instinct to keep me out of danger. The tension comes from the inability to relax. Everything you do and say has to be thought out, and that really does take it out of you.

I was worried too about the effect that the work was having on my family. I was away from home most of the time and I could never give any reason for my evenings at the 'shop'. My explanation for being out late so often was that I was so tied up with the Trade Delegation contract that I had to spend time in the evening catching up on the factory's other business. The excuse was plausible because the factory was doing well. Mike was doing his bit by steering various domestic double-glazing jobs my way, often from his col-leagues in the police, and, of course, having a prestige contract like the Soviet Trade Delegation did bring in other commercial work too.

93

As the firm was prospering, I was able to buy treats for the family, but when I paid for them to have a special evening out, I often could not go myself. It did not make for a very contented home life but I managed to persuade everyone that it was only a short-term thing and that the company had moved up into a new level of prosperity which I could not afford to neglect.

Occasionally, I would manage a break but mostly it was a relentless grind of work and de-briefing. I would keep myself going with a few drinks and console myself with the thought that I was doing a worthwhile service for my country – and one which no one else could do in my place.

Then I would flag again and Jay would watch me and say, 'Oh by the way, Bill, do you want to hear about your Biker?'

I would drag myself upright and say, 'Yes, of course I want to hear,' and Jay would smile and say, 'Oh yes. He's another winner for our collection. His beat is the London School of Economics.'

Then of course, he knew he had my attention and over a glass or two of scotch, he would give me the whole story.

Our Biker did indeed have a motorbike, one with laundered plates supplied by the same South London car dealer. He used to live the life of a radical student at the LSE, with every detail right, except that he wasn't actually doing any work. He was, of course, not known to be Russian. He was enrolled as a Polish exile, and despite his biker's appearance, he always had lots of money for drinks and was a ringleader in organising the wilder parties at the college. That part was important, Jay said, because most of the students he mixed with were well-to-do also. 'He picks his friends very carefully,' Jay said, 'and he specialises in foreigners. It won't surprise you to know that he has a special affinity with Libyans and other Arab visitors.'

The Biker collected information about Libyan activities in London, and those of other Middle Eastern countries which used students to take part in and support terrorist activities in Europe. He was also engaged in talent-spotting, that is selecting students who might be willing to serve the Soviet cause, either as students in London, or more likely later, after they had graduated and moved into influential positions.

His talent-spotting extended to British and other European students as well. Student days are a good time for noticing weaknesses in the future great. An indiscretion, or worse, committed in a politician's time at the LSE can be very awkward when 'revisited' on him or her in later life. There was in addition the simple role of observing the student population and deciding who among them, if any, had genuine pro-Soviet feelings which could be developed through tactful cultivation.

At the beginning of an evening like that I would often feel quite jaded, but by the time Jay had finished his tale, I would perk up and think, 'Oh, what the hell. I can't stop now. I can always rest when this is all over . . . '

CHAPTER 9

It was during the third stage of the contract – the double-glazing of Millfield Flats – that I started to make use of children to obtain information. If I had come across more children earlier in my work I might have had some scruples about making use of them, but by now I had grasped that the Trade Delegation was a warren of intelligence activity and I was prepared to use any methods I could to help expose it.

My first try was with a young girl called Martia. I went routinely into a flat on my list and found that she had been left alone there by her parents to let me in and make sure the furniture was properly covered with dust-sheets. She was a bright, pretty girl of about fourteen and she spoke halting but quite good English. I said we wanted to do the bedroom first with the main room afterwards and I found that she had everything prepared for us. Once the fitters had started, I didn't have very much to do, so I sat with her at the dining room table and found she was quite talkative.

I asked her if she had been into London often and whether she had seen Buckingham Palace. She said she had and she told me about her school and how she had been given the day off so that she could be in the flat to meet us. I asked which pop stars she liked and once again Cliff Richard turned out to be the favourite. On an impulse, I said, 'Do you have a record player?' and when she said she did, I asked her if she would like me to get her some records. I made up a story about having a friend who was given reject records free which were still of excellent quality. She really brightened up when I said I would see if he had any of Cliff Richard's.

That won me a nice cup of tea and over that I asked her 'And what does your Dad do?'

She told me that he worked outside the Trade Delegation and that his speciality was engines. She didn't say what kind

96

of engines and I was in two minds about whether to continue. I was sure I could get her to tell me, without much difficulty, but at the same time, I didn't want her reporting to her parents that I had been asking a lot of questions.

Later, she told me without prompting that her mother was a typist in the administration block, but I deliberately did not pursue that and contented myself with making Martia feel at ease with me. The approach paid off quickly because once the chaps had finished the bedroom window they fancied a cup of tea also, and while Martia was making it, I slipped into the bedroom. Under the guise of checking on the work my men had just done, I went into my usual routine and sneaked a look under one of the dust-sheets at what I judged from its shape to be a desk. The first thing I found was a manual marked Vickers Aircraft Corporation! I rifled through a stack of papers and saw several technical drawings also marked Vickers and others headed Rolls Royce. There was no time to get all the details, but I noted the title and number of the Vickers manual and noted the code numbers of as many of the plans as I could remember. To avoid arousing suspicion I rejoined the men, then I made an excuse to slip down to the boiler house to write down the numbers which I had been repeating over and over in my head all through the conversation in the dining room.

I gave them to Jay at the evening de-briefing and told him all about my conversation with Martia. I also told him about the records and Jay agreed that it would be a good idea to keep my promise. Russians are great ones for doing things methodically and if Martia had been given the day off school to let us into her parents' flat, it was likely that the pattern would be repeated. If I could win Martia's friendship with a couple of records, the word would not take long to spread through the classroom.

'Mike can shop for the records,' Hay said. 'I'm more worried about these blasted machine drawings. You can bet what you like they have no business being in the Trade Delegation.'

'There's not much doubt about that,' I said, 'but if you want me to follow this up, you'll have to be quick. I can't spin the work in the flat out much longer than a couple of days at most.'

'Right,' said Jay. 'I'll be in touch with Vickers tonight. You make some excuse to be late on the site tomorrow and ring Mike before you go in. He'll have instructions for you.'

I did as I was told and the message Mike passed on was urgent: 'Find out anything you can about the drawings in the desk and get more numbers.' The manual was highly classified and Vickers had no idea it was missing.

To explain my lateness at the Trade Delegation, I arrived in a mini-cab and wore a suit instead of my usual working clothes. I explained that I had had to go and see a manufacturer to chase up some missing materials; no one made any comment and I made my way back up to the flat.

Martia was there again, sitting on the settee, and she didn't seem to be paying any attention to my fitters who were now working in both the bedroom and the main room.

It could have been worse, but I wasn't entirely happy with the prospects. Though Martia was in the living room, there was no guarantee she wouldn't suddenly get up and go next door. Anyway, Kevin was outside the bedroom window, going up and down the ladder.

I had no choice but to try – Jay didn't send urgent messages lightly – and I walked into the bedroom and set to work under the steely eye of Lenin. Many of the rooms in the Trade Delegation were decorated with portraits of Lenin but this one was a particularly menacing one as it reflected blue in some lights and red and blue in others, with the result that the eyes seemed to be moving.

I was just about to take a look at the desk, when Kevin's face appeared at the window. He gave me a wave and all I could do was wave back and move away from the window. With Lenin watching on one side and Kevin on the other, I really didn't have much choice.

I did notice by the bed, though, that there was a photograph of Martia in some kind of uniform. She was in a group of girls of her own age, all wearing red skirts with white blouses and red bandanas, presumably the uniform of some kind of Soviet youth organisation, and beside it in a smaller frame was a photo of a couple I took to be her parents.

Kevin had vanished again from view, so I took a close look at the photos and tried to remember as clearly as I could the features of the parents. Then I went back into the dining room, Martia made tea and we chatted about her records.

I said I would bring them to her the next day and I asked if she would be there. She said she would be at school but would be home by half-past three. I said we would probably be in the next door flat by then and she could collect the records from Kevin if I wasn't around. Martia was really pleased about that and we chatted for a while longer. Then I said I had to check a window so she settled down on the settee with a book. It looked like being my last chance, so I did not waste time.

I went into the bedroom and after a quick check that Kevin was down below, at ground level, I whipped up the dust-cover on the desk and started to sort through the plans and drawings. This time, I wanted to get down more numbers than I could trust to memory, so I used a pad and managed to get most of them. I still felt I had some time to spare so I went through the drawers and in one I found a bundle of personal letters. Over the months we had had a lot of success with letters, especially as people tend to be very frank when they are writing to family and close friends from far-away places. I this case, I hoped there would be some clues to the identity of the man who had access to such sensitive technical drawings, but I knew that whatever I stole would have to stay stolen; there would almost certainly be no opportunity to put any-thing back. The pile was thick and tempting. Would a couple be missed? I decided for once to stick my neck out. If I couldn't pick the man out of Jay's album, the letters might well be the only way to determine his identity. I took two letters out of the middle of the pile, slipped them into my jacket, closed the drawer and went back into the dining room, just in time before Kevin appeared on the ladder again. I had done as much as I could and I just hoped it would be enough for Jay.

As it turned out, it was, but this was one occasion when I couldn't really say that Jay was pleased. He did identify the man and he did confirm with both Vickers and Rolls Royce that none of the drwings should have been off their premises, but, as he said, that wasn't much of a consolation. There was nothing to be done. There was no proof of how he had come by them; it was doubtful that he would try and strike in the same places again, and Jay never did find out who his contacts were. All in all, it was rather a hollow victory, though it did at least lead to a tightening up of security at both aircraft plants.

Round about the same time, we had another curiously unsatisfactory outcome to lead for which, for a while, I had high hopes.

I was working my way systematically through the flats, continuing my regular 'search and observe' routine, when Denushenko asked me to interrupt my schedule to do one particular flat that was not on my list. When I went up there, I found the flat was empty, but it was being equipped with new furnishings and one look told me the occupant was going to be someone special. Most of the flats in the Millfield block were quite nicely furnished and while we were there, a whole load of new furniture was bought. It led to a very amusing incident, in passing, as we came into the grounds one day to find a team of Russian labourers breaking up really nice pieces of Victorian furniture and throwing them into a skip. My men went beserk at the sight of the waste and begged me to ask Denushenko if they could be allowed to take the furniture off his hands. The answer was a polite but firm no: nothing was to be allowed to leave the Trade Delegation.

The furniture going into this flat, however, was of a very different order and to underline the extra status, carpet was being laid instead of the usual lino. One other detail completed the picture: two men were scrubbing the sink as though they were preparing for the CO's inspection and I grinned at Valerya who was my escort for the day and said, 'Looks as though you've got a big noise on the way.'

Valerya shrugged. 'Someone from Moscow,' he said. 'They've got everyone jumping around.'

Jay didn't need to tell me to keep an eye on this one and I made my preparations as best I could. While we were working on the window, I slipped an expensive ratchet screwdriver behind one of the cupboards and I also made sure that we started work on another flat on the same landing so I could keep an eye on developments.

The flat remained empty for three days, then I saw signs of movement. Naturally, that was when I discovered that my valuable screwdriver was missing and I asked Valerya if we could go back to the VIP flat. Valerya didn't seem unduly bothered and he escorted me up and knocked on the door.

It was opened by a man who had the unmistakable look of a leader and Valerya showed him noticeable deference. He was in his mid-forties with slightly greying hair and he wore a suit that looked as though it had come from a top-flight London tailor – quite unlike most of the clothes I had seen around the Delegation.

Without understanding the conversation in Russian, I gathered he had asked what we wanted, and when Valerya told him he invited us in with quite a friendly gesture. In the bedroom, there was a heavy nap overcoat lying on the bed, with a well-polished briefcase beside it and a pair of white gloves. I noted these details and took a good look at the man's features, then found the screwdriver and left, thanking him profusely. Predictably, as a short-term visitor, he was not in Jay's album, but the next day I managed to get the number of the car that had been assigned to him and that was enough for Jay to pick up his tail. The outcome was an intriguing little mystery that we never really got to the bottom of.

He began with a sight-seeing tour of London by limousine, which took in the Tower and various other landmarks, then he dismissed his chauffeur in the City and took a taxi to a private club on the Embankment. Jay's people watched him closely and were disturbed by the fact that the Russian – though he had only just flown in from Moscow – seemed perfectly at home in the club, which was one favoured by MPs and senior government officials for their contacts with the business world. The membership rules were extremely strict. As Jay said, 'I couldn't get past the door myself without being signed in by a member,' but the Russian walked through the lobby, with a nod to the porter, and made his way straight to the dining room.

101

'If he's a member, I'd like to know how,' Jay said. 'And if he isn't, I'd like to know what the hell the club thinks it's playing at. A lot of people use that place on the assumption that everyone's been vetted and can be trusted. I'll bet some of them would have had kittens if they'd known who had just dropped in.'

I knew that what irked Jay was the idea that the Russian was apparently able to conduct business and reestablish a network of commercial contacts without anyone being aware of it. To have access to a club like that presupposed that he had a lot of contacts and friends in high places – unknown to MI6. One of Jay's concerns was always to keep a good sense of the patterns of Soviet-British relations; which firms the Russians were dealing with, what kind of economic relations they wanted to develop. British businessmen and diplomats had no freedom in Moscow to develop links with their Soviet counterparts, yet this man apparently was free enough to flip in and out of London and to move in circles that were entirely unknown to the authorities.

I was disappointed myself mainly because I had hoped I had uncovered some secret negotiations which Jay didn't know about, but I had a consolation prize soon afterwards which more than made up for it.

I was back on my routine schedule and in one flat – Flat 22 – we came across two more children, a little girl who was again called Martia and her brother who never told me his name. They were friendly enough kids, but having them both in the flat together cramped my style considerably. I could not look in drawers or go through papers so I had to content myself with browsing round the more obvious objects in the room, where I noticed that several of the decorations were souvenirs of Wales. There were two figurines in Welsh national dress and a set of tea mats on the table with pictures of Welsh landscapes.

I said to the little girl, 'Oh, you like Wales do you?' and she answered without thinking, 'Mummy and Daddy go there at weekends. We've never been. And they go to Shropshire too.'

She added the last part as though she didn't know where or even what Shropshire was; it was said more in a tone of pride

102

at having remembered a rather difficult English word.

I didn't ask for more details, but the remark set me thinking. Why should the parents of young children spend their weekends in Wales alone. These kids were just the right age to appreciate excursions in the Welsh countryside and Russians were supposed to be very family minded. I might not have thought much more about it, except that the next day I found myself alone, briefly, in the bedroom, and I came across a map. It was an ordinary road map and when I turned it over I saw that it was of Wales and North-West England. On the top someone had scribbled 'Royal Hotel, Chester,' together with a date.

I didn't have my hands on the map for more than twenty seconds but it was enough to start an investigation which had far-reaching implications for Jay. It took some time, but he finally reported that the couple had been identified through the hotel and their movements traced on that weekend and several others. They were indeed enthusiastic Welsh tourists, but it came as no surprise to me or to Jay that the beauty spots they were visiting all happened to be conveniently near defence installations. Once again I was delighted to have been the one to trigger off the inquiries. As we had long since recognised, that was one of my most valuable functions; without the inside knowledge I was able to provide, keeping track of the movements and various activities of the Trade Delegation staff would have been impossible.

Meanwhile, while Jay was doing the follow-up investigations in Wales, we moved on to a section of the flats that my men had been looking forward to – the part which housed all the young, unattached secretaries. Their part of the building was a wooden-clad structure built on top of the Millfield block, almost like an extension added onto the roof. Denushenko explained that this was the accommodation for the single girls who worked as typists in the Trade Delegation and in some cases at the embassy in Kensington, and he asked me to give two days' notice when we were preparing to do a specific flat so that the girl in question could be given a day off work to prepare it for us.

My lads were keen to get cracking as many of the girls were

extremely attractive, but then workmen on building sites the world over are optimists and their efforts to chat the secretaries up certainly didn't lead to any great love affairs. I had a lot more success up there than they did – but then I was looking for information, not romance!

The first flat we worked on belonged to a very attractive young woman with Nordic blue eyes and fair hair, but she was stand-offish to the point of being icy which did not bode well. Fortunately, I quickly got to know a much more amenable young woman called Olga who was in a very different mould. Olga was dark-haired, petite and lively, and she never missed a chance to have a chat; most of the girls had been chosen for their skills in English but Olga was exceptionally fluent and she had a very quick mind as well.

We began with the usual chit-chat and I discovered she didn't have any inhibitions about talking about her life in England, or in the Trade Delegation, and she was very funny indeed on the subject of the elderly woman who acted as their unofficial 'mother'. From the way Olga talked about her, wardress was probably closer to the mark, and when I met her myself I had to agree that she certainly was a forbidding old biddy. While we were double-glazing her flat I don't think she took her eyes off us once, and you would have thought she was paying us by the minute – out of her own pocket! Throughout the process, she did not say a single word, and it was not difficult to see that she would be a difficult 'mother' for the girls to cross.

Their life did not seem too bad though, but their main problem apparently was loneliness. The girls were carefully supervised at home and in the office; those who worked outside the Trade Delegation travelled together in a minibus and their leisure activities on their days off were also arranged for them. It was, by Olga's account, quite a busy life, but they were very much cut off from the main stream. They entertained each other in their rooms, drinking always – for some reason I never fathomed – Earl Grey tea, and spent most of their time gossiping about their boyfriends back home in the Soviet Union.

Olga's boyfriend was doing his military service and she told me this was very much the usual pattern. She said many of the secretaries chosen for work abroad had been recruited after service in the Soviet Youth organisation, and a high proportion of them seemed to have met their boyfriends that way too. As Olga seemed very free and outspoken, I decided to chance a pointed comment to test her reaction.

'Do they pick girls with boyfriends in the army so they'll have some kind of hold over you?' I asked.

I expected an argument, in fact I more or less said it to provoke one and Olga didn't disappoint me. 'No they're not controlling us,' she flashed back, 'we're just as free as you are.' Then she smiled, and added with a grin, 'They just like to know we have someone to go back to, that's all.'

Because of the arrangement that had been made for the girls to be there while we worked, I had virtually no opportunity to search their rooms, but I discovered quite by chance that Denushenko had taken that privilege for himself.

I saw him for the first time on a wet afternoon when I had sent the chaps down to the boiler house for a break. I had decided to remain upstairs and was sitting in a little cupboard room which housed a reserve generator, with the door slightly ajar, looking down the landing.

Denushenko came up the stairs and made for one of the rooms we had already finished. I knew no one was there because Olga was the only person on the floor and I watched Denushenko let himself in with the pass key.

As there would be nothing suspicious about my being seen on the landing, I decided I would saunter down and have a look. I walked quietly past the door and Denushenko did not notice me because he was too busy riffling through the dressing table drawers. About a week later, I caught him at it again and this time he was reading one of the girl's letters. It really was pretty despicable behaviour for a hero of the Soviet Union, but I decided I wouldn't bother telling him not to trespass on my patch!

Jay did not raise an eyebrow when I told him what Denushenko had been doing. 'I'd have been surprised if he hadn't,' Jay said. 'He'll be bound to have to report on the girls and their letters are his best source of information.'

He was not as relaxed however about the next piece of information I gave him: that Olga worked in the embassy in Kensington as secretary to Captain Zotov, the naval attaché who was expelled for spying.

The fact itself did not worry Jay unduly, and neither of us expected to get anything from Olga about Zotov's activities. What irritated Jay was that when I identified Olga in the album, he found that she was listed in the Home Office file as Zotov's wife.

'God, they're at it again,' Jay said. 'They used to do it all the time but we thought we'd managed to stop them. They list all kinds of people as phoney wives; it's their way of getting in extra staff above their permitted quota, and of providing decoys sometimes, when they don't want us to keep track of them.'

In the end though, we did get value for money out of Olga and once again, it was by pure coincidence. It began with Olga having a little grumble about their leave arrangements. She told me that secretaries were allowed home leave once every three years, which was true of most of the staff in the Trade Delegation, but there was a strict hierarchy about the way in which the travel was arranged. The workers, she said – and she used the word in a way which implied that she meant those, like herself, who really did the work – had to make the channel crossing by ferry then go overland by train, with the travel time being deducted from their precious leave. Senior staff went by air, which gave them a much longer vacation at home, and the top people went one better and went by sea – only their cruise through the Mediterranean to the Black Sea was added to their holiday, not deducted.

In itself it was an interesting minor sidelight into Soviet attitudes, but what made it important was that the subject only came up because Olga had been helping two of her friends pack.

Later, I went downstairs and saw some crates outside the entrance to the flats which obviously belonged to the girls who were going on leave. They were being loaded onto a furniture removal van and I found an excuse to hang about and watch. The van had the name of a London company on the side and I automatically made a note of it, together with the licence number. Two men were doing the loading and they didn't seem to be having a hard time, as they were swinging the crates up without breaking into a sweat. I thought nothing of it – I presumed the girls didn't have all that many belongings – then I noticed two more crates being brought across from the administration block with what seemed to be identical markings to the ones with the girls' effects.

They were of similar size too, but the men did not swing these into the van. They were in fact so heavy that they had trouble getting them on board, even using the van's hydraulic loading platform.

When I talked it over with Jay, neither of us had many doubts about what was going on: something was being shipped out 'unofficially' mixed in with the personal effects. Jay said he would tip off Customs and Excise, but we thought it would probably be another annoying little dead end. I didn't see how I could follow it up, but sometimes threads link up by chance, and as it turned out, they were not the last crates of that type that I was destined to see.

It happened some time later, when we had finished with the secretaries' flats and were back in the main block, working our way through the schedule. We came to one flat which seemed particularly well-appointed. It was also very tidy, as though the woman there was especially proud of being a good home-maker, but the most striking aspect of the flat was that most of the decorations had some connection with India.

These were not just a few cheap souvenirs, like the ones that had been collected in Wales. This couple seemed to have lived in India for some time and had brought back expensive ornaments, including religious figures, paintings and several pieces carved in ivory. Another point I noted about the flat was that most of the books in the bookcase were on the subject of aeronautics, but I didn't have a chance for a thorough search, as the woman was there most of the time. In the course of several conversations, I confirmed that India had been their last posting, but I didn't question her about what they had been doing there, as she seemed exceptionally alert and quick-witted.

I then met the man himself once and identified him in the album, but the rest of the details were, surprisingly, filled in by Valerya who happened one afternoon to be in unusually communicative mood.

I mentioned the Indian ornaments and said they seemed like a very nice couple. 'Oh yes,' Valerya said, off-handedly, 'they were there for a long time. He was in charge of a factory which made MiGs for the Indian government.'

When I told Jay, he absolutely exploded. 'Do you know what his job is listed as in our files?' he said. 'Store manager! He's supposed to be in charge of the shops selling Russian artefacts in Holborn and Finsbury Park.'

I couldn't help smiling. I knew it was one of Jay's pet hates to feel he had been taken for a sucker when the Russians filled in their applications to enter the country.

But this particular web was not yet complete; there were more strands to be woven, and Jay did come out on top in the end.

I was well on with the Millfield Flats when I was summoned to Denushenko's office and asked if I would mind quoting for some extra work in the main administration block. I was delighted, as we had done no double-glazing in there at all, and I dearly wanted to have a look. I didn't realise how lucky I was going to be however until I went to the first room listed for a window replacement.

It was a large room at the side of the administration block and was obviously used primarily as a storage area as there were far more packing cases in it than furniture. They were all identical in shape and markings to the ones I had seen being loaded with the secretaries' personal effects, and most of them had a word stencilled on them that I had come to recognise – MOSCOW, in Russian script.

Amazingly, the guard who escorted me didn't bother to stay. I couldn't believe my luck and knew this was one chance I must not miss. I was there to measure up the room and as I had taken my toolbag with me I whipped out a small crowbar and started to lever open the crates. A look inside the first one was enough to tell me that I had hit a jackpot – but one that was not going to please Jay. The crate was full of what were obviously pieces of technical and scientific equipment. Most were in their original packaging and all were British made. Some had come from as far afield as Scotland, and many of the manufacturers were well known as Defence contractors. I made notes furiously, logging names and references and making quick pen sketches of some of the more striking pieces of equipment.

A lot of the stuff in the second crate seemed to be optical equipment including some giant size lenses in superbly turned metal frames, and it did not take an expert to guess that the items in the third case were mostly to do with weapons.

I managed to stay in the room for more than an hour, collecting enough information to keep Jay busy – and hopping mad – for several weeks. It wasn't often that I had such a good streak and it really seemed to be my benefit afternoon. On top of everything else, there was one interruption which provided me with another crucial part of the jigsaw – a man wandered down the corridor, fortunately noisily enough to give me ample warning, and it turned out to be the MiG assembly man from India.

When Jay had completed his inquiries, there was no longer any mystery about why such high-powered aeronautics experts should have apparently been demoted to the lowly task of looking after craft shops.

The merchandise for the shops – combined with the personal effects of embassy staff – provided the necessary cover for the shipping out of this vast range of products representing the best in British technical expertise.

The room was a treasure house of technical and scientific know-how, and the fruits of countless 'shopping' trips by experts in the Trade Delegation – including, Jay told me furiously at a later de-briefing, what amounted to a complete do-it-yourself assembly kit for a fighter aircraft's missile sight which, as he put it bitterly, had not been bought over any counter.

Much of the equipment had probably been obtained

legitimately, but there were also innumerable items which must have been stolen or obtained by false pretences; for example they might have been ordered through a company which appeared to have the necessary clearances in order to buy sensitive equipment. MI6 would now face the mammoth task of trying to locate the contacts, perhaps sympathetic or even unwitting companies who had helped to convey this kind of equipment into Soviet hands.

The discovery set in motion a very serious tightening up of precautions against industrial espionage – especially among defence contractors. It was one of my most productive afternoon's work, and ironically it was the one during which I came closest to being caught.

In almost two years inside the Trade Delegation, I was never spotted carrying out my undercover work. I had some very hairy moments but I was never actually seen prying, even though I spirited out scores of pieces of evidence in my toolbag, briefcase and duffle coat.

That afternoon, though, I was almost caught out – and it was by the youngest lad in my factory who was helping out part-time.

I was so absorbed in what I was finding in one of the crates that I didn't hear him come into the room – mainly, I must say in my defence – because he was wearing ghastly 'brothel-creeper' shoes with inch-thick crêpe soles.

I had a crate well levered open and my head and hand right inside. I thought my cover was finally blown but thank God he assumed the worst – by his own lights. He assumed I was in the process of nicking something, and as boss of the factory, he took it as my privilege.

He gave me a conspiratorial grin and said, 'Better watch it, Bill, you'll get us all thrown off the job.'

I felt like knocking his head off his shoulders for his cheek, but I was also relieved that his imagination didn't stretch to anything worse.

The lad has left my factory now and taken a job with British Rail, and to this day he doesn't realise that he is the only person to have actually seen the 'double-glazing spy' at work!

CHAPTER 10

As the contract reached its final stage, I began to wonder how my mission inside the Trade Delegation would end – assuming, of course, that I managed to remain undetected. Everyone was delighted with the information we had already obtained and if nothing else came out, the operation would still be regarded as a total success. Personally, though, I did not want it to tail off. I wanted to end on a high point, but I could not see one in prospect – until the Russians kindly stepped in themselves to provide a climax: by trying to recruit me for their side!

It began with the arrival on the scene of a man called Zigarov. Supposedly, he was one of the new batch of guards but it was obvious from the outset that he was different; he just wasn't a typical member of the boiler house gang. In the first place, he was much too well dressed. Several of the guards wore suits, but Zigarov's was much better cut, almost to the standard of the senior people in the Trade Delegation. He was altogether too confident for his age – which must have been about thirty – and this trim, dapper little figure simply did not fit the normal pattern.

His approach to conversation was different too, as within the first couple of meetings, he was talking about politics, a topic that had not been raised by a single other person since I had begun work. The chat started off in the normal, neutral way. I was still talking about my plan to go to Moscow for the Olympic Games, assuming the contract was finished in time, and that usually led to a wider discussion of sport in which my men and the rest of the new guards joined.

Then one day, quite soon after our first meeting, Zigarov said casually, 'Tell me, Bill, what do you think of Mrs Thatcher?'

I tried to duck the question and give a vague answer, but

111

Zigarov would not let the topic rest. He asked me the question again and this time he put it even more bluntly:

'Are you a Thatcher supporter, Bill?'

'Oh no,' I said, 'I'm on the other side. Labour through and through,' remembering gratefully my doctored official file which had me listed as pink with distinct tinges of red.

'Do you think most British people support Mrs Thatcher?' Zigarov went on. 'She is not liked by the Russian people. They see her as a friend of America.'

I answered much as before, trying not to be too positive, but leaving Zigarov in no doubt that I saw myself as a man of the left.

During the course of the following days, it became obvious that Zigarov was paying special attention to me. After one conversation about the Olympic Games, he gave me a complete set of the first issue of Olympic stamps and when I said how much I appreciated them, he came back with an Olympic coin.

Then, one bright, sunny afternoon, I was sitting on the grass outside the main building and Zigarov came over and joined me.

'I understand you like a drink, Bill,' he said, almost giving me a sly wink. 'Would you like to have one with me? I like a trip to the pub myself.'

It was a first, as Jay instantly recognised. It was not particularly surprising that the outgoing group of guards should have mentioned my liking for a drink. Nevertheless, this was the first time that a Russian had been the one to propose a meeting outside the Trade Delegation. Up to that point, I had always been the one who had to make the running. To test him, I said, 'Sure. I'd love to have a drink. In fact, why don't we send out for a few cans? The contract is well in hand and I'm feeling a bit thirsty.'

It was obvious straightaway that this was not what Zigarov had in mind. 'No Bill, not during the day,' he said. 'I prefer to go to the pub. What about tonight, after work? They open at half-past five.'

From the way he said it, I knew beyond doubt that I was now dealing with a different style of Russian. People like

Gariachi and Valerya were fairly at ease with the English pub and its ways, But Zigarov had clearly been around and was much more experienced.

This was born out when we did go to the pub and he handled himself like an old stager. He chose the pub – The Jubilee – set up the drinks and ordered crisps and nuts as though he had been born to it. We were to have a good many pub meetings in the days to come and I only saw him slip up once. It was then that I was reminded that so much of his expertise was consciously learned and wasn't coming naturally. We were in a pub in Kentish Town and he strode up to the bar, smiled at the landlord and said, in a confident voice, 'A pint of Guinness for my friend here and a pint of Ben for me.' You would have thought from his tone that an English boozer was his second home – except that he hadn't noticed it wasn't a Truman house!

In The Jubilee, however, he was complete master of the situation and I could see that the evening had been carefully stage-managed. 'I hope you like the pub,' he said casually, after the first round of drinks. 'I wanted to invite a friend to meet you, and we've been here together before. I wanted to make sure he found us all right.'

When the 'friend' arrived, I recognised him long before he joined us at the bar. Zigarov's eyes had hardly left the door and I could sense his relief when the man finally showed up.

The new arrival was someone I had never seen at the Trade Delegation. He was older than Zigarov, about forty or so, and there was no likelihood of ever mistaking him for an Englishman, even at a casual glance.

His clothes were definitely continental, as were his manner and general appearance. He had on a leather coat with broad lapels and a belt which tied loosely without buckles. When he opened it, I saw he had another leather garment underneath, a kind of sleeveless waistcoat, partly unbuttoned, over a loud open-necked shirt. Imitation crocodile shoes completed the picture and he had expensive jewellery on both hands, probably five or six rings in all, and a gold bracelet which hung down over one wrist.

Zigarov did the introductions, giving the man's name as

Yuli. In the conversation which followed, two things stood out. The first was that Yuli obviously had not just been told about me, he had been briefed in detail. He didn't ask any of the questions about me that I would have expected, because he clearly knew the answers already. The second was that Yuli was the boss, a fact that came through just standing at the bar. When it was time for Yuli to buy a round, Zigarov took care of it, and he did it with the air of someone working to a prearranged budget.

I pretended to ignore all this byplay of course and concentrated on being friendly towards Yuli. I said I was very pleased that my men seemed to be getting on so well with the Russians in the Trade Delegation and I mentioned that I had never seen him before anywhere in the complex.

'I don't go down there much,' Yuli said. 'I live in Crescent Road, in Crouch End. We have some flats there.'

I admit I was a bit taken aback as that is very close to my own home, especially when Yuli reeled off a list of pubs he used and nearly all of them were on my list of locals. He mentioned one in particular with a Scottish landlord that I thought I knew very well. 'Did you know Alec served with the Russians in Iceland during the war?' Yuli said. 'We often have a chat about those times.'

'I didn't know that,' I said, truthfully. 'Has Alec ever mentioned me?'

'No,' Yuli said, 'but I don't go there all that often. I usually drop in there early, when it's empty and Alec likes to chat about the war.'

'As you're so near,' he added, 'you must come round to Crescent Road for a drink.'

I thought I had better keep up my usual business front so I said, 'I'd like that very much. Maybe there's some double-glazing there that needs doing.'

'Perhaps,' Yuli said, 'but I don't deal with that sort of thing. My business is oil.'

I wanted him to go into more detail, but Zigarov interrupted and turned the conversation back – yet again – to Mrs Thatcher. This time it would have been obvious to a child that I was being invited to go through my left-wing party piece

114

for Yuli's benefit and I didn't let Zigarov down.

When I reported the evening's exchanges to Jay, he was absolutely jubilant. 'You're being set up,' he said. 'They're actually setting you up. It's time we thought a bit ahead. Turn the conversation round towards the factory and tell them you do a lot of work for the government. Leave the details to me. I'll organise you a good yarn.'

As always, Jay kept his promise diligently, and it was just as well he acted quickly as Zigarov kept up the pressure.

Within days, they proposed another meeting, this time for a lunch-time drink. I made a show of resisting at first. I said that Mr Denushenko always insisted that I remain with my men at all times and I didn't like to take long lunch hours. 'I do slip out for a quick one occasionally,' I said, 'and I sometimes have to go out for materials, but I try not to make a habit of it.'

Zigarov just laughed. 'Materials, Bill, or a few cans of beer?' he said. 'Anyway, don't worry about Denushenko. He likes a drink himself. He won't mind if you have a break with us. Let's go to The Old Crown in Highgate. We can use one of the Trade Delegation's cars.'

As it was Friday and pay day, I had to make some emergency arrangements. I called the factory and arranged for someone else to go to the bank. I was speaking from an open line in the administration building, so I said pointedly that I was sorry to land them with the chore at the last minute but I was going out for a meeting that might be important for future business.

When we got to the pub, Zigarov bought the drinks and before I was halfway through my first pint, we were back on Mrs Thatcher again. It was beginning to go beyond a joke, now, going through my speech for the third time, but I played dutifully along and eventually I managed to get the conversation round to factory business.

Yuri asked me how the factory was doing, and I said, 'Very well, especially as the Trade Delegation contract has been such a terrific boost.' They commented on how well the contract was going from their point of view and that gave me the opening I wanted. Following the scenario Jay had laid out for me, I said, 'Well, my chaps are quite used to this kind of work, especially after all our jobs for the Ministry of Defence. In some of the places we've been in, the security's been even tighter than at the Delegation.' I added with a grin, 'Sometimes we have so many different passes, we could deal a hand of cards with them.'

I could see Yuli's eyes literally widening, so I eased off a bit and let Zigarov do the prompting.

'What kind of places are these, Bill?' he asked.

'The worst was an amphibious warfare establishment, near Piccadilly,' I said, pretending to have a good grumble. 'It took you half an hour just to get through the security checks and the parking round there was diabolical too. And the worst of it is,' I said, 'you don't make much profit at the end of the day. You have to give so many backhanders. The nice thing about the Russian contract is that nobody has to be paid off.'

'So it's like that is it, Bill?' Yuli said. 'It's the same in America too.'

'You've been to America, have you?' I asked him.

Yuli started to tell me about his travels on oil business in Arizona and Canada, but it wasn't long before Zigarov got us back to the point.

'You have a lot of trouble with bribery, do you?' he said.

'Yes,' I replied. 'I've just had a real bad one. I've never been so glad to finish a job. So many bottles changed hands, it's a wonder we made a profit at all.'

I had had quite a few drinks by now and I deliberately let them see that they were loosening my tongue nicely.

'The man in charge was virtually a dipso,' I said, 'even though he was in a very senior position.'

They wanted to know what position and I said I didn't know exactly but judging from where he worked, it must be something very high up. Having worked at the Ministry of Defence, I was on safe ground, and I gave them chapter and verse of the office 'arranged' by Jay, even including the detail that he was authorised to use the cabinet door. To insiders that was a real sign of status at the MoD and I managed to convey that to Zigarov and Yuli, without being too specific.

After a while I decided I had gone far enough for one night

116

and I pretended I had realised that I had been a bit too free. I mumbled something about not knowing any more and turned the conversation back to one of my uncles who was liberated by the Russians from a prisoner of war camp in Germany. It was a story I had told before in the Trade Delegation and it had always gone down well – especially when I mentioned how the Russian troops had shared their rations with the starving prisoners. It had the advantage of being true, and this time I gave them his name and the correct date, so they could check if they wanted to, and I mentioned, to make it easier, that my uncle had served on the Allied Control Commission after the war.

'Well,' Yuli said finally, 'I've really enjoyed the evening. You must have a drink at my home. I'll get in touch with you at the Trade Delegation.'

I did not have to wait long and I must say the Russians were a bit obvious about their next move.

Two days later, out of the blue, Denushenko himself came over to where I was working and asked if I could deal with an emergency problem.

'I'd like you to go over to our flats in Crescent Road, Crouch End,' he said. 'We have a fault with a patio door.'

Here we go, I thought, now that's what you call a coincidence. 'Right,' I said, 'I'll go tomorrow morning and I'll take a factory fitter with me.'

That seemed to satisfy Denushenko and I went to Crescent Road the next morning, and as instructed, rang the bell at Flat Number One.

We were let in by a stunningly attractive woman in her mid-forties and shown into the most luxurious flat I had seen anywhere since I started work for the Trade Delegation. I learned later that the oil specialists lived in a world apart – with a standard of luxury deliberately geared to the level of the British, American and Arab oil people they were doing business with. This was my first taste of it and it was quite a shock after the humdrum accommodation at the Trade Delegation. There were no wooden chairs and sheets of old lino here. The flat was ultramodern, with sleek comfortable furniture. In one corner of the lounge there was a kitchen-cum-breakfast area, completely enclosed in glass, with a suction-fitted door and expelair fans to ensure that no cooking odours escaped. The kitchen was like a miniature stage set with ceramic hobs and every conceivable modern appliance, ready for the cook to perform for the guests, if necessary, but I could not imagine this woman spending much time at the sink.

Her world was Liberty's, Harrods and the boutiques of Bond Street, and her attitude to the patio door repair was of a lady of the manor forced to dabble in trivia.

Superficially, the door did not seem to be badly damaged, but when I inspected it, I found the problem was worse than it looked. I told her that it could be repaired temporarily but to make it properly secure, it would need a new frame and that might be a problem, as the installation must have been done at least ten years ago. I said I would contact various suppliers to see if the frame was still made; otherwise I would have to install a completely new door.

She listened but she clearly wasn't interested. 'I was just asked to get it fixed,' she said. 'Please do whatever is necessary.'

I said politely that I would certainly do my best but I would have to contact Mr Denushenko as he was the one who paid the bills.

'Don't worry about that,' she said, off-handedly, 'just make the arrangements.'

So far it was going exactly as though there had been no ulterior motive behind my summons to Crescent Road so I decided to test the water.

'A chap called Yuli lives here, doesn't he?' I said. 'I wonder if he's around.'

'He lives in Flat Nine, Bill,' the woman said, straightaway. 'Wait a minute, I'll go up and see if he is there.'

I almost laughed out loud. This was getting obvious to the point of being ridiculous. At no stage had anyone used the name Bill, so the welcome mat had obviously been dusted off already.

The woman went upstairs and Alan, the fitter, went out to the van to get his tools. I never like to waste a moment alone, so I took a quick look at the address and the memo book that was sitting beside the hall telephone. I could not do much, but as I had my pad in my hand already for taking details of the window repair I copied down the first five numbers in the book, just to keep my hand in.

When she came back, she said, 'Yuli is there. He'd like you to go up for a drink.' I followed her upstairs and there the stage was set, with Yuli relaxing in shirt sleeves in another luxurious flat, similar to the one below.

'So,' I said, 'we're meeting sooner than we thought.'

'Yes,' Yuli said easily, 'as a matter of fact it was my idea. We were talking about you and what you were doing at the Trade Delegation and someone said, "Couldn't we have him fix our door too?" '

'I can fix it all right,' I said, 'but I had better have clearance from Mr Denushenko.' I always took every opportunity to show that I was a little bit nervous of Denushenko and always seeking his favour, but Yuli brushed my concern aside. 'I'll give Denushenko a ring,' he said, 'you just relax and have a drink.'

We talked a bit about the oil industry in the Soviet Union, then Yuli said suddenly, 'Is it true you are thinking of coming to Moscow?' I said I certainly hoped to and told him how fond I was of all sports, including athletics.

'I'm a great sports fan too,' he said. 'Especially football. I have been to several first division games over here.'

From sport, the chat drifted towards business again and I had the impression that we were working through a checklist of questions.

'Do you belong to a trade union, Bill?' Yuli inquired, *à propos* of nothing in particular. 'They are very strong in the building trade, I believe.'

I said they were but I didn't belong to one myself. 'I'm very sympathetic to unions,' I said, 'but you know how it is. Being the governor, I can't really belong to one myself. I negotiate all the contracts, and a lot of firms wouldn't do business with us if they thought the boss was in the union too.'

Yuli seemed satisfied with the answer and I felt that he had got his green light to move onto the next stage.

'How about another night out?' he said. 'I hear the pubs in Kentish Town are pretty good.'

This was my chance to take a hand in the arrangements as I knew Jay was concerned that he had not so far got any pictures of Yuli and Zigarov. 'The Wrestlers is nice,' I said, choosing a pub that was well placed for observation.

Yuli agreed but I had reckoned without one little problem – when he arrived at our next meeting, he turned up in full motorcycle gear. I had never thought of him as a motorcyclist and neither had the MI6 camera team. They had been briefed to watch for a man in a leather jacket with rings on both hands; instead, all they saw was the back of a man inside a crash helmet and visor.

When I expressed surprise, he said, 'I often use a bike to get through the traffic. It's hell in the rush hour around Kensington.'

That evening and two or three subsequent ones passed off with no great advances being made on either side. Yuli was obviously proceeding cautiously, but I began to sense that he was nearly ready for his big move. I was sure I had passed most of my 'tests'. I was left-wing, anti-Thatcher, pro-Russian because of my family's personal experiences; I was grateful to the Trade Delegation for making my firm prosperous and I was on drinking-buddy terms with several members of the staff. I was Irish, not English, and I didn't have a very high opinion of the British senior civil service. There wasn't much more I could do to make myself an attractive target; it was now up to them.

By this time, I was intensely curious to know how they would make the actual approach. The ground was well laid – or so it must have seemed to them – but it is always tricky to make the jump, to bringing the first actual suggestion of betrayal.

Yuli finally chose him moment in The Crimea and he came at it so obliquely, he caught me by surprise.

'Do you know anything about medicine, Bill?' he said.

At first, I didn't see the point of the question.

'How do you mean?' I said. 'It's not really my field.'

'Well, it's just that the Soviet Union is always interested in developing its medical expertise,' Yuli said, 'and if you ever came across any information about medical developments, we'd be very interested.'

I said that was a bit too far out of my line, but Yuli was not to be put off.

Did I know anyone in medicine? Anyone concerned with developing new drugs or cures? Anything that might help save lives?

'We have this problem,' he said innocently. 'If we ask questions about technical matters, it is misinterpreted. We are only interested for humanitarian reasons, but people do not believe that. But if we talked about such matters, we could exchange information, as friends.'

So there it was. I had my come-on. It wasn't exactly subtle, but if I had wanted to sell information, I had been given a rough-and-ready rationale. I was careful not to appear too enthusiastic, but I didn't fend them off either. Jay had told me to take the middle way and that was exactly how I handled it.

Jay laughed heartily when I told him about the medical angle. 'I like the humanitarian cause bit,' he said. 'You wait till you've given them your first bit of medical information, then see what you'll be asked for next.'

Despite the joking though, Jay briefed me extremely carefully and we went over all the likely ways that the approach could develop.

'Whatever you do, don't press too hard,' Jay said. 'Remember, they are softening you up. You're not softening them. Don't play hard to get. Just don't play at all for a while and see what they do next.'

The meetings in The Wrestlers and The Crimea continued, interspersed with sessions in the boiler house. I waited patiently, and Jay recorded the various stages on tape and film.

Finally, Jay got a bit impatient. 'I think we may as well nudge them along a bit,' he said. 'They're dying to get their claws into you. Let's see if we can prod them into action.' He briefed me carefully and at the next pub session I started to grumble again.

'I'll have to be late at the Trade Delegation tomorrow,' I

said. 'I've got to go and see that damned chap in Whitehall again. He's got another job for me, but it's going to cost me, as usual. What annoys me is that he never actually comes out with what he wants. I wouldn't mind if he said, 'Can you let me have a couple of hundred? He says snotty things like "I presume my fees are arranged," and I'm supposed to take my cue from that.'

I was apparently well-oiled by then and I was working up carefully to the moment Jay had planned.

'That man Armstrong is a real pain in the arse,' I said. 'I wish I'd never done business with him in the first place.'

The name had been dropped and Yuli, to his credit, did not twitch a muscle. I knew he was doing exactly what I would have done; repeating the name to himself several times so he would not forget it during the conversation.

I knew they would follow it up, and inside Whitehall they were ready for it. Armstrong was a real person, with an office exactly where I had described it in the MoD and a dreadful personal history which would start coming out as soon as anyone inquired.

Though Yuli didn't mention the actual name, I could see that my dropping it had made him bold. In his terms, I had gone over the top, and he was determined not to let me retreat.

'Is this job in the same place as before?' he asked. 'The amphibious warfare place you were telling us about?'

'No,' I said, 'and I'm damn glad it isn't. I don't want any more work down there, thank you.'

I was leading with my chin deliberately now and Yuli did not waste the opening. He asked me again about the place and persuaded me to describe it.

I told him there wasn't much to describe really. It was just a building near Piccadilly with a big experimental tank in the basement and a lot of technical equipment.

The information I gave was long out of date, but I was able to make the description sound convincing as I had seen the establishment, when it had existed, during my earlier days at the Ministry of Defence.

I gave them a step-by-step run-down on the security

arrangements, emphasising that it took contractors like myself half an hour just to get into the building.

I could see that Yuli was really getting excited but he was not yet ready to go the last mile and come right out into the open with me.

Again on Jay's instructions, I was the one who finally brought the issue to a head.

Yuli had proposed a lunch-time drink, apparently on the spur of the moment. We were geared up for these surprise meetings by now as Jay was determined not to have any gaps in his photographic record.

Yuli suggested going to The Jubilee again and I managed to warn Mike to get the forces marshalled, as Jay used to say.

We ordered drinks, settled into a quiet corner, and Yuli straightaway started asking me again about the various government places I had done work for.

'Yuli,' I said, 'I've been doing a lot of thinking about the questions you've been asking me and I think there's a bit more to you than you've told me. I don't think oil is all you're interested in. Now, I don't mind having these chats,' I said, 'but I don't want to get into trouble. My own chaps are beginning to wonder about all these meetings we have. I'm afraid one of them is going to start saying I'm getting too friendly with you, and word might just get to our security people.'

Yuli was a bit taken aback by my frankness, but he did his best to reassure me.

'The only reason we ask you these questions,' he said, 'is that we like to keep up with things. Your people do the same in our country. You have the same beliefs as ourselves. You are part of the Labour movement. All you are doing is helping the side you believe in.'

We were now well over the hump. We weren't talking about medical information any more and we both knew it.

'Look Yuli,' I said, 'I might be able to help, but I'm not sure how to go about it. I do go to the kind of places where I might be able to read documents, but I've never done anything like that before, and I'm not sure what to do.'

The good Lord didn't strike me dead for a liar at that

123

point, so he must be on our side, and Yuli was lapping it up.

'But I'm no fool,' I went on. 'I know what you're asking. I know we have the same beliefs but business is business. What's in it for me?'

Yuli handled that one nicely. He didn't come right out and talk about payments. He went into a little speech about how the Soviet Union always took good care of its friends. Naturally, he said, it would depend on what kind of information I managed to provide, but for example, if I did come to Moscow, he could make some very special arrangements to make sure I enjoyed myself in any way I wanted.

So the terms were set out and I was now on Moscow's books. I was ready for them to come to me and I knew I was laying myself open to an approach that could well come in the distant future. That was the Soviet way, Jay said. 'They'll let you "sleep" now. They'll decide when they're ready for you – and we'll be ready too.'

It was a fitting way to end my time at the Trade Delegation but I decided it was prudent to skip the Olympic Games! I only hope they appreciate that I didn't ask for any fees for providing them with Mr Armstrong. After all, I felt I owed them a farewell present for the best contract my company has ever had.

EPILOGUE

Eventually, the contract had to come to an end. I dragged it out for as long as I could but finally, I had to report to Jay that I could not find any more excuses for remaining inside the Trade Delegation. I had had last minute supply delays and I had put the 'finishing touches' to the work several times over, but I really had come to the end of the line.

Jay was prepared for the moment and we closed the 'shop' with as little fuss as when it had opened. We had one last meeting which was part de-briefing and part celebration, but there was no riotous champagne party.

We ended with a typical touch of Jay's dry sense of humour. He handed me an envelope with a substantial final payment, and said, 'I suppose you'd better sign for this.'

I was a bit taken aback as I had not signed anything throughout, then I saw Jay's grin and he said, 'Don't worry, just put your code-name, Blue. I'll tell the accountants that will have to do.'

His thank yous, were equally brief, but I appreciated the warmth he put into them. I had acquired a great respect for Jay over the time we had worked together, and he made me feel it was mutual.

'Bill, you're a lad and a half,' he said. 'You've got the front and you've got the guts. The stuff you've collected for us will keep my chaps working for years. I don't think even now you realise how much harm you've done the KGB in Britain. All I can say is thank you from the British government.'

Even at such a moment, I had to pick him up on one point.

'Jay, you don't have to say British government. Just thanks from the government. Don't forget I'm a Britisher. A loyal Northern Irelander. It's my government too.'

Jay smiled and apologised and admitted how easy it was to make that kind of mistake.

Luckily, it was one the Russians made on a much more serious level, and I have always been convinced that it was one of the biggest single factors which kept me undetected.

I have no doubt at all that picking a mainly Southern Irish crew for the double-glazing work was a sound basic move. Nevertheless the Russians should have been more discerning. Throughout all the months of listening to my boys telling them tales of Dublin and the Wicklow Hills, they never once drew the distinction between the North and the Republic – and I suppose I must be grateful to them for that.

I believe they failed to spot me also because of another very simple error: they allowed themselves to be taken in by superficial appearances. From the moment I walked into the Trade Delegation to the moment I walked out of it, I was, to them, an ordinary Irish working man, with a duffle coat and scruffy shoes, who liked a joke and a chat and was a bit too fond of his drink.

In all the chat in pubs and in the boiler house they never even tried to go beyond that façade. I never had to make any great effort to conceal my true background. The reality is that I was brought up in a tradition of strict discipline, family discipline in the home first, polished up by my years in the forces and the security services. The Russians, thank God, never even tried to probe below the surface.

There is no doubt too that having people like Mike and Jay behind me enabled me to keep up the front with confidence. It may be a cliché to say it, but without backup you can trust, this kind of operation can very quickly turn sour.

Mike's contribution was enormous, not only in practical ways but in helping to keep me sane and cheerful, even when I was almost out on my feet with tiredness. Typically, though, when it was over our own private celebration was even less emotional than my parting with Jay.

'Well,' he said, 'You did all right. I got my promotion. A nice lift-up, so we'll be friends for a while longer yet.'

I just grinned and ordered him another pint. With someone you trust as much as Mike, all the serious stuff can be left unsaid.

One of the satisfactions of being able to tell this story now

126

is to reveal the existence of men like Mike and Jay who work to protect the country quietly – and above all, efficiently.

A great deal is said and written about the times when our national security breaks down. There really is no way of avoiding that: moles, double-agents and security flaws make headlines, the successes, by definition, have to remain in the shadows.

For once, though, the story of a success can be told and I believe it can only do good if it makes people more aware of the extent of the intelligence war going on around them. My operation had contributed, directly or indirectly, to several expulsions. It had helped identify a number of Soviet agents and establish the kind of activities they were engaged in – ranging from direct espionage against military installations to economic intelligence-gathering in Britain, as well as subversive activities in the Jewish and exile communities in London. It had pinpointed the enormous part that the Trade Delegation, as opposed to the military side of the embassy, was playing in intelligence matters, and it had also provided a fund of knowledge about the day-to-day workings of the Soviet community in England – knowledge that had never previously been accessible.

Whatever anyone says, the Russians are as active as ever but it should be reassuring to know that, on our side too, there are some people who are awake.